LAUGHT

Four Comedies For Large Casts
Bill Tordoff

**HEINEMANN
SPOTLIGHTS**

Heinemann Educational Books

Heinemann Educational Books Ltd
Halley Court, Jordan Hill, Oxford OX2 8EJ

OXFORD   LONDON   EDINBURGH
MADRID   ATHENS   BOLOGNA
MELBOURNE   SYDNEY   AUCKLAND
IBADAN   NAIROBI   GABORONE   HARARE
KINGSTON   PORTSMOUTH (NH)   SINGAPORE

ISBN 435 23901 5

Printed in England by Clays Ltd, St Ives plc

CONTENTS

INTRODUCTION

I wrote the plays in my first collection, *Play it for Laughs*, in response to the need I found for plays which would give a large group of young people the experience of putting on a play together. I found that most short plays had a small cast, often of one sex. They also tended to be literary rather than dramatic.

So I decided to write the sort of plays I could not find elsewhere. I wanted them to be lively and to have parts for everyone in a mixed class.

The success of *Play it for Laughs* encouraged me to write the four further plays in this collection. They too have parts for a nominal cast of a dozen or so girls and the same number of boys. Inevitably all the parts are not of equal importance, but everyone is a character with individual lines as well as choruses to join in.

Although the scripts were all written for performance they can, of course, be used for class reading or as the basis of work in Drama.

NOTES FOR THE NOVICE DIRECTOR

Preparation

If you want to change the plays to suit your class, feel free! You may want to increase or decrease the number of parts by sharing out lines differently. You will almost certainly need to re-allocate parts between the sexes, changing names as appropriate.

Make sure that you work out moves and groupings of characters before you start to rehearse, even if you have to modify them later.

Acting

In these large cast plays, only a few of the cast will be speaking at any given time. As director, you need to remind your cast constantly that acting consists not only of saying lines but in remaining in the part throughout. (When not speaking, actors will not go far wrong if they look at whoever is speaking, their expressions showing their reactions.)

When individual lines are being spoken by members of a group, it helps to draw the audience's attention if an actor moves slightly as he or she starts to speak.

Learning a part

Once the cast know how to say their lines and when to move, they can learn their parts. They need to learn to speak their lines clearly and with feeling, on cue and with the appropriate moves. They need to learn not only their own lines but also the lines or choruses spoken by a group.

Later rehearsals

Throughout rehearsals the actors need to speak as loudly as in performance. To ensure this, conduct later rehearsals from the back of the room.

Once scripts are down rehearsals should begin to approximate to performance, using props and costumes. In plays of more than one scene, practise going straight from one scene to another, striking and setting scenery and props very quickly. If production is to go smoothly it is vital that properties (or their substitutes) are used in rehearsals. Actors need constant practice both to remember lines and to cope with important props such as the model Ark in *Crime Wave* or Arthur's sword in *2B Or Not 2B*.

Above all, keep reminding yourself that despite the inevitable difficulties and frustrations in rehearsals, it is all worthwhile. There are few feelings more pleasant than the elation (and relief!) when your cast take their final curtain call.

B.T.

CRIME WAVE

CHARACTERS

The Noah Family

NOAH	MRS NOAH	
SHEM	SARA	*their wives*
HAM	RUTH	
JAPHETH	REBECCA	

The Workers

Seniors	*Adults*	*Kids*
OLD MAN 1	MAN 1	KID 1
OLD MAN 2	MAN 2	KID 2
GRANNY 1	MAN 3	KID 3
GRANNY 2	MAN 4	KID 4
GRANNY 3	WOMAN 1	KID 5
GRANNY 4	WOMAN 2	KID 6
	WOMAN 3	
	WOMAN 4	

SCENE: The Noah Tripe and Ferret Works
TIME: The Present

NOTE ON CHARACTERS

Most of the characters are numbered rather than named, to simplify doubling and re-allocating of lines, but all have individual personalities, as can be seen by studying their speeches. For instance, OLD MAN 1 is deaf but cheerful, GRANNY 4 is moralistic, WOMAN 1 is a leader, KID 5 is adventurous, and so on.

Scene 1

A table or rostrum with jugs and mugs. Benches. At one side, a telephone. Hammering off-stage. The phone rings. JAPHETH *enters and picks up the phone.*

JAPHETH: Hello. Noah's Tripe and Ferret Works. Sorry, we never work on the Lord's day. Ring back tomorrow.

> *Enter* SHEM.

SHEM: What time is it, our kid?
JAPHETH: Dinner time.

> *More hammering. They stare off.*

SHEM: What's our dad doing?
JAPHETH: Dunno. He's been locked in his workshop all morning.
SHEM: He used to give us the strap if we worked on the Lord's day: it's very odd.
JAPHETH: We live in very odd times.
SHEM: Right.

> *There is a shot off-stage. They look.*

SHEM: Our kid, shooting an intruder.

> *Enter* HAM *with a gun.*

SHEM: Did you get him, our kid?
HAM: No. Scared him, though. One of them vandals from the council estate. Stealing tripe.
JAPHETH: They say some of 'em are starving, 'cause they've no work.
SHEM: That's not our fault.
HAM: They're mad, intruding in daylight.
JAPHETH: It's like the weather: forty days sunshine and no rain. It isn't natural.
HAM: It's natural in Africa.
SHEM: And Spain.

JAPHETH: I know that! We don't live in Spain or Africa, do we?
We live on the biggest tripe-works and ferret-farm in England.
And hot weather is not natural here. Rain's natural.

HAM: I like it hot.

Enter MRS NOAH.

MRS NOAH: Where's your dad?

SHEM: In his workshop, our mam.

MRS NOAH: Typical! Your wives are all ready to serve dinner,
but Mr Clever has to be woodworking on a Sunday. What will
God say? And what's he making, anyway?

SONS: Dunno.

MRS NOAH: If we don't serve it soon, it'll spoil.

NOAH *is heard whistling a hymn-tune.*

JAPHETH: He's coming.

MRS NOAH: Thank the Lord. I'll tell the girls.

Exit MRS NOAH. NOAH *enters, whistling and carrying a large
roll of paper.*

SONS: Good day, father.

NOAH: Good day, lads. Is dinner ready yet?

JAPHETH: The womenfolk are bringing it.

NOAH: About time.

Enter MRS NOAH, SARA, RUTH *and* REBECCA *with the
meal.* ALL *stand at the table.*

NOAH: Bless these fruits of the earth, O Lord, and us thy
servants.

ALL: Amen.

ALL *sit and start eating.*

HAM (*taking a mouthful*): Oh, no! Not ferret pie again!

MRS NOAH: I thought you liked ferret pie.

HAM: For a change, yes. But not every blooming day!

NOAH: Language! (*Taking a drink and spitting it out*) And what's
this flaming stuff?

RUTH: Iron drink.

NOAH: Why is there no beer?

RUTH: You know very well, father-in-law. We're short of water.

MRS NOAH: We need a good downpour.

RUTH: There's hardly enough to water the ferrets. We can't wash tripe and we can't brew beer.

JAPHETH: So where did you get this stuff from?

Silence.

NOAH: Well, where's it from?

REBECCA: I swapped it for some stale tripe.

NOAH: Who with?

REBECCA: A woman from the housing estate.

NOAH (*standing*): I don't believe it! My own daughter-in-law! How often have I told you all to keep away from outsiders?

MRS NOAH: That's right.

REBECCA: She said she needed food for her children.

SHEM: 'She said'. Haven't you learned yet that they're all liars?

HAM: And thieves. I shot at one this morning.

REBECCA: They can't all be liars and thieves!

NOAH: How many of them will be worshipping the Lord with us in the Temple this evening?

REBECCA: Not many, I suppose.

JAPHETH: Not one.

RUTH: They never worship the Lord.

ALL: Never.

MRS NOAH: They never wash their clothes.

SARA: Except on the Lord's day.

SHEM: They never dig their gardens.

HAM: They breed like rabbits.

RUTH: They throw stones at animals.

JAPHETH: They leave prams on railway lines.

SARA: Dog dirt everywhere.

RUTH: Stealing.

MRS NOAH: Swearing.

HAM: Fighting.

SARA: Litter and graffiti everywhere.

REBECCA: Everywhere?

ALL: Everywhere!

> ALL *sigh and shake their heads.*

MRS NOAH: When will it all end?

NOAH: In a month.

ALL: How do you know?

NOAH: 'Cause God rang last night.

MRS NOAH: I thought you were on the phone a long time! How is he?

NOAH: Oh, he's all right: he always is. But I was telling him about the heat and the water shortage and all the crime.

JAPHETH: Doesn't he know? I thought God knew everything.

NOAH: 'Course he knows! I was just reminding him. He said the heat was a present for our Ham, 'cause he'd been praying for it.

RUTH *(to HAM)*: So we've you to thank for that!

HAM: Well.

NOAH: And I told him about the people on the housing estate all being criminals and vandals and asked him if he couldn't do anything about it. He said he'd give it a think and come back to me.

REBECCA: And has he done?

NOAH: I should say he has! *(Holding up the paper)* I found this on the doorstep. He's got all his buttons on, has God. This'll kill two birds with one stone.

RUTH: What good will killing birds do?

ALL: Shh!

NOAH: Here is God's remedy for the water shortage *and* the crime wave. Soon the earth'll be perfect again, like it used to be in the good old days.

HAM: Good old God!

MRS NOAH: What a relief! What is he going to do?

NOAH: Don't move: I've a surprise for you!

> *Exit NOAH. JAPHETH unrolls the plan, looks at it, reverses it*

and studies it. NOAH re-enters, carrying a model Ark about 18 inches long, inverted. It is clumsily built, like a barge with a flat-roofed house on top. The hull is white and the superstructure black, with a row of square windows. NOAH puts it on the table, still inverted.

NOAH: That's what I've been making. What do you think of it?

Silence. ALL look at each other.

SARA: Very nice.

ALL: Mm.

NOAH: That is a model of God's answer to the world's problems!

HAM: Pigeon loft, is it?

NOAH: How can you solve the world's problems with a pigeon loft, stupid? Come on! Can't you see what it is?

ALL: No.

NOAH: Can't you guess?

Silence.

ALL No.

NOAH: That is a boat, isn't it?

ALL: A boat?

NOAH: Yes, a boat. And it's called the Ark.

He sticks a big flag saying ARK on the under-side.

RUTH: It's a funny boat, isn't it?

HAM: Won't float, that. Will it, our kid?

SHEM: No, it's unstable: it'll capsize.

NOAH: No way will it capsize! God planned that: he does not get things wrong!

JAPHETH: Dad!

NOAH: God has told me to make a boat like this . . .

JAPHETH: Dad!

NOAH: Because it is going to . . . What?

JAPHETH: It's upside down.

NOAH: Don't be stu— Upside down?

JAPHETH: Yes, look.

He removes the flag, reverses the Ark and sticks the flag in the top.

JAPHETH: See?

The OTHERS *applaud.*

REBECCA: You made it wrong way up, Father Noah.
NOAH: I know, I know! I was just, er, testing you.

ALL groan in disbelief.

NOAH: Anyway that is the boat that God says we have to build, here and now.
SARA: But the sea's fifty miles away: a boat's no good to us, is it?
ALL: No.
NOAH: All agreed?
SHEM: The Lord's got his wires crossed this time. Boat-building is the last thing we need.
NOAH: All know better than the Lord, do we? Right, I'll tell you how this boat is going to save us all.
SHEM: How big will it be? What's the scale?
JAPHETH: Erm, oh, here. 'One cubit equals fifty feet.'
NOAH: This model is a cubit long.

He measures it from elbow to finger-tip.

HAM: A fifty-foot boat, eh?
NOAH: Right! Now, all keep quiet about this! Promise?
ALL: Promise!
NOAH: Right! God is going to turn on the taps in heaven, and he's going to leave 'em full on. It's going to rain for forty days and forty nights.
HAM: Non-stop?
NOAH: Non-stop.
HAM: Well, I'll . . .
ALL: Language!
HAM: What about horse-racing and pigeon-shooting?
MRS NOAH: And how will we get the washing dry?

ALL begin to talk at once. NOAH bangs on the table.

NOAH: Listen! Every river in England will rise and burst its banks. A massive wave of water will sweep over the whole country. Over the highest mountains! All crime and badness will be swept away!

RUTH: Aw. Will it cover all the TV masts?

NOAH: Of course it will!

RUTH: There'll be no telly, then? It *is* serious.

NOAH: And God says we've to take all the animals in the boat with us.

REBECCA: Which animals?

NOAH: Well, I suppose he meant the ferrets, and Shem's whippet and my pigeons.

SARA: And the cats?

NOAH: Yes. He was really insistent about taking all the animals.

REBECCA: My terriers won't take up much room, nor their new puppies. Aw, they are lovely.

WOMEN: Aw!

JAPHETH: When's this rain going to start, dad?

NOAH: In a month, exactly.

SHEM: A month! We can't make a fifty-foot boat in a month! What do you think, Japheth?

JAPHETH: Well, it says here: 'Any DIY enthusiast can assemble this simple houseboat in just a few evenings with the aid of a few ordinary tools.'

SHEM: We'd better write out an order for the wood, and get down to the timber yard first thing.

MRS NOAH: And we'd better start freezing food and sorting clothes. Come on.

They start to rise. The phone rings. JAPHETH answers it.

JAPHETH: Noah Tripe and Ferrets. Oh, yes, he's here.

He puts his hand over the mouthpiece and turns to NOAH.

JAPHETH: It's God!

NOAH: What's he want?

JAPHETH: I don't know: you talk to him! *(On the phone)* He's coming, your, er . . . your worship.

NOAH *(on the phone)*: Yes, sir? What can I do for you, sir? Yes, I've just shown them the model. They're er, quite excited about it. Yes, the plans are here, sir.

He frantically beckons: JAPHETH *brings the plans.*

NOAH: Scale: yes. A mistake, is there? It should read: 'One cubit equals 500 feet.' No problem! Thank you very much, sir. The family really appreciate all you're doing for us. The animals? No problem, sir. What? Could you repeat that, sir? Two of each. I see. Would that include elephants, sir? Of course. And snakes? Naturally. What about fish? Silly me! Of course not! Well, thanks again. And you have a nice day, sir.

He puts down the phone, shakes his head and sits. ALL *are staring.*

JAPHETH *(altering the plan)*: Five hundred feet long?

NOAH *nods.*

MRS NOAH: And what was all that about animals?

NOAH: We have to take two of every kind.

MRS NOAH: Every single kind?

RUTH: Pandas?

HAM: Pigs?

SARA: Hippos?

SHEM: Hyraxes?

REBECCA: Rhinos?

JAPHETH: Raccoons?

NOAH: Cross-eyed skunks. The lot.

MRS NOAH: Who's going to tend all that lot?

NOAH: We'll all have to muck in.

MRS NOAH: We'll all have to muck out, an' all! Well, I suppose the Lord knows what he's doing, though why he can't just send a normal downpour, then kill all these criminals with some lethal disease I can't imagine.

SHEM: Dad, there's no way we can make a five hundred-foot boat in a month, even working overtime.

HAM: He's right, dad.

SARA: Ring God back, Mr Noah. Tell him you can't do it.

NOAH: Ooh, I daren't.

SARA: You must.

NOAH: Shall I?

ALL: Yes!

NOAH *crosses to the phone, then stops.*

NOAH: I don't know his number.

JAPHETH: Ring enquiries.

NOAH: Right. Hello? Town? Erm, Heaven. God. G-O-D. Oh, ex-directory. No hope of getting him. I see. *(Replacing the phone)* We're finished. We'll never make a boat so big in a month. We'll all be drownded.

JAPHETH: No! I've an idea! Clear the table, you women!

He puts the plan on the table as the WOMEN *clear it and go out.*

JAPHETH: We'll get it built on time. The bow over here. The stern right over there. Come on, and I'll explain it all.

They go out. A few bars of music suggesting speed and activity lead into:

Scene 2

A whistle blows.

SHEM *(off)*: That way!

The eight ADULTS *march on.*

SHEM *(off)*: Stop there!

They stop and look round.

WOMAN 1: Years since I've been in here.

WOMAN 2: We used to work over there dressing tripe.

WOMAN 3: Mm. Before they mechanised it.

WOMAN 4: I used to feed the ferrets. I hated 'em.

MAN 1: We used to put 'em down apprentices' trousers.

Laughter.

MAN 2: Forget the ferrets. What is this job we've signed up for now?

MAN 3: Dunno. There were trucks stacked with timber bombing through our estate first thing.

MAN 4: Perhaps it's new sheds.

Enter SHEM.

WOMAN 3: Shh: Mr Shem!

SHEM: Pin your ears back! You lot are Construction Squad A. You'll be assembling joists *(pointing)* over there: sawing, drilling, knocking pegs in, ten hours a day, starting at seven. Half an hour for lunch, quarter of an hour break morning and afternoon, finish at six, £1.50 an hour, week in hand, no work—no pay. Any questions?

WOMAN 3: Is there a canteen?

SHEM: Any more questions?

MAN 2: How long will this job last?

SHEM: Completion date: a month from yesterday.

MAN 2: Why is that?

SHEM: None of your business.

MAN 3: What are we making?

SHEM: I've told you: assembling joists.

MAN 3: Joists for what?

SHEM: Any more questions? Good. Line up. Left turn. To that pile of timber: quick march! Left, right! Left, right!

SHEM *and his squad march out. Off-stage at the other side we hear* JAPHETH *leading his squad, picking up* SHEM's *rhythm.*

JAPHETH *(off)*: Left, right! Left—oh, no!

Enter JAPHETH.

JAPHETH: Hurry up! Make it snappy!

The SENIOR CITIZENS *enter, walking slowly, some with sticks.*

JAPHETH: Rest here!

They stop.

JAPHETH: Good morning.
ALL *(except* OLD MAN 1*)*: Good morning!
OLD MAN 1: What does he say?
OLD MAN 2: Good morning.
OLD MAN 1: Oh. Good morning.
JAPHETH: You all know who I am?
ALL: Mr Japheth!
JAPHETH: That's right.
GRANNY 1: Is it the tripe again?
JAPHETH: No, you'll be sewing canvas this time, old lady. And splicing ropes.
GRANNY 2: Is it for tents?
JAPHETH: Could be.
GRANNY 3: I heard your father was enquiring about animals.
GRANNY 4: Yes, are you setting up a circus?
JAPHETH: You'll find out. Now, you'll be working here, so you'll be able to sit down.
OLD MAN 1: What?
OLD MAN 2: Sit down.
OLD MAN 1: Oh, thank you.

He sits.

JAPHETH *(shouting)*: When I tell you!

OLD MAN 1 *leaps up, startled.*

JAPHETH: This isn't a holiday camp! Any more questions?
ALL: No!

JAPHETH: Good. We'll move over there – *when I say!* – to collect our materials. Line up. Turn. Quick march! Left, right! Left, right!

They march off. Off-stage, HAM *picks up* JAPHETH's *rhythm.*

HAM *(off)*: Left, right! Left, right!

Enter HAM *and his squad: six teenage* KIDS, *not marching, some chewing.*

HAM: Halt! Stop!

They stop and stare at him.

HAM: Right, listen to me. My name is Mr Ham.

KID 1 *snorts with laughter.*

HAM: Anything funny?

KID 1 *shakes his head.*

HAM: Good. I'm in charge of you lot. You've to saw up those rods over there *(pointing)* and fit them into frameworks.
KID 2: What are we making: a prison?
KID 3: I've heard it's a zoo.
OTHERS: Yeah.
KID 4: What are you building a zoo for? Don't you make enough with tripe and ferrets?
HAM: Money's always useful, isn't it?
KID 4: Don't know: I've never had any.
HAM: Be an experience for you, then. You'll remember it as long as you live.
KID 1: I don't know what to spend my wages on.
HAM: Put it away for a rainy day.
KID 1 *(looking up)*: Big laugh.
KID 5: Are the others making a zoo as well?
HAM: I've seen you before.
KID 5: Not me.
HAM: You lot don't need to know anything.

KID 6: Why not? Why all this secrecy?

KID 2: I've heard we have to finish in a month.

HAM: Right.

KID 3: What's the rush?

HAM: We've had a long-distance weather forecast: fine weather for another thirty days.

KID 1: Then what?

HAM *(shouting)*: Do you want this job or not?

KID 1: Suppose so.

KID 2 *(raising a hand)*: I was thinking . . .

HAM: You're not paid to think: you're paid to work! All alike, you housing-estate louts: bone-idle! We're starting now: come on!

He walks off, followed by KIDS 1–4.

KID 6: Was he the bloke that shot at you yesterday?

KID 5: Yeah. I'll get my own back.

KID 6: I don't like the smell of this place.

KID 5 *(sniffing)*: Ferrets.

KID 6: Worse than ferrets. Something's wrong: I smell a rat.

HAM *(off)*: Hurry up, you two!

KID 6: Keep your eyes open, kid.

They go out. A few bars of music suggesting monotonous work lead into:

Scene 3

Hammering offstage. Enter the ADULTS carrying wood. They chant:

ADULTS: Days and days we've been a-working,
  Days and days we've hammered and sawed.
  Noah never catches us slacking or shirking:
  Friday payday brings reward.

They march off. Enter the SENIORS with canvas and rope. They sit and chant as they work:

SENIORS: It's not so very easy living when you're getting on,
'Cause the pension's not the only thing you get.
You get galloping phlebitis, you get rheumatoid
arthritis—
Then the doctor says it's something that you ate!
He advises peace and quiet and he puts us on a diet;
But he doesn't understand we're very poor,
So we're glad to get this job and to earn an extra
bob
Splicing ropes and sewing cloth for Mr Noah.
But the younger ones, they shock us
'Cause they cheek the boss and mock us
And they ask what is the use of what we do.
And all that we can say is we live from day to day
And we trust to Mr Noah to see us through.

A whistle blows. ALL *stop work except* OLD MAN 1.

OLD MAN 2: Morning break.
OLD MAN 1: What?
ALL: Morning break.
OLD MAN 1: Oh. I wonder if it's time for break yet?

Enter REBECCA *and* SARA *with drinks.*

REBECCA: Morning break!
OLD MAN 1: I told you!

The ADULTS *enter as* REBECCA *and* SARA *give out the drinks.*

REBECCA: Everybody happy?
ALL: Yes!
SARA: All got a drink?
ALL: Yes, thank you!
GRANNY 1: The youngsters aren't here.
REBECCA: They're just finishing a job on the deck.
GRANNY 2: The deck? We're not making a ship, are we?
REBECCA: Er, no, I didn't mean the deck: I meant the, er . . .

SARA: The decoration.

REBECCA: The decoration. Painting, you know.

GRANNY 2: Oh, right. I say, we'd look stupid making a ship up here, wouldn't we?

Laughter.

OLD MAN 2: We'd have to push it all the way down to the river.

MAN 1: Unless the river flooded right up here.

MAN 2: By the time it got up here, most everybody'd be drowned.

Laughter.

MAN 3: Not much use us all working, if we're going to get drowned!

MAN 4: They say it's a good way to die.

WOMAN 2: Better you than me!

Laughter.

REBECCA *(loud)*: Oh, do stop talking like this!

Silence.

WOMAN 2 *(to MAN 2)*: You've upset her now, with your silly talk of drowning. I'm sorry, miss.

REBECCA: Nobody's going to drown! None of you!

SARA: Of course they aren't. Come on, Rebecca: come and lie down. *(To the OTHERS)* She's worried about her puppies!

WOMEN: Aw!

SARA *and* REBECCA *go out.*

OLD MAN 1: What's up with her?

OLD MAN 2: She's worried about her puppies.

OLD MAN 1: Oh. Has she seen the doctor?

Laughter and groans. Enter the KIDS.

KID 3: Give me a drink: I'm gagging.

KID 4: My throat's as dry as charcoal.
KID 2: It's all that sawdust.
KID 1: Hey, leave us a drink!

The KIDS scramble for their drinks.

WOMAN 2: Have you finished painting?

The KIDS stop and stare.

KIDS: What painting?
WOMAN 2: Miss Sara said you were painting.
WOMAN 1: Decorating.
WOMAN 2: That's right, decorating.

The KIDS look at each other and shrug.

KID 3: We've been sawing planks.
GRANNY 1: Haven't you done any painting?
KID 3: No, we never do.
GRANNY 1: That's strange!
MAN 3: Shh!

Enter SARA and RUTH.

SARA: All finished?

ALL nod and watch silently as SARA and RUTH clear the drinks away and go out.

MAN 3: I'll tell you what: everything about this job's strange.
GRANNY 2: How do you mean?
MAN 3: Well, what are we supposed to be making? Has anybody seen any plans?

ALL look at each other. Silence.

GRANNY 3: We don't need plans. Bosses tell us what to do: that's good enough for us.
GRANNIES That's right!
MAN 4: It isn't right: it's wrong!
GRANNY 4: Why is it wrong?

MAN 4: Because any construction job needs plans. Noah's not making this up out of his head, but he never shows us plans. Why not?

OLD MAN 1: What's he on about?

OLD MAN 2: Plans.

OLD MAN 1: Oh, flans. I like gooseberry best.

ALL: Not flans: plans.

Laughter.

MAN 1: You're right. You can make something small without a plan, like a stool or a box, but for a big job like these sheds you need a plan.

KID 2: What sheds?

MAN 1: Well, what are we making, then?

Silence.

MAN 1: Does nobody know what we're working on?

MAN 4: It's like a barn, isn't it, mainly?

ALL *agree.*

MAN 4: With like floors in.

KID 2: Barns don't have floors in, do they? And what about all these cages we've made?

GRANNY 1: For animals.

GRANNY 2: Livestock.

GRANNY 3: Ferrets!

KID 3: Ferrets! Some of those bars are four inches thick!

KID 1: They're for monster ferrets, then.

Laughter.

KID 3: The Mighty Noah and his giant ferrets!

Laughter.

KID 4: The Mighty Ham and his giant hamsters!

Laughter.

GRANNY 4 *(standing)*: I'd just like to say that I am disgusted with
you youngsters!

SENIORS: Hear, hear!

GRANNY 4: When I think of all the trouble you used to make
on our estate, hanging round all day. Our lives were a misery!

SENIORS: Hear, hear!

GRANNY 4: You should be grateful that Mr Noah has given us
all good jobs. But what do you do? Criticise and question!

GRANNY 3: Right! We're working-class, and God put us on his
earth to work, not to think.

SENIORS: Hear, hear!

   Enter NOAH.

NOAH: All happy at your work?

ALL: Yes, thank you, Mr Noah.

NOAH: Break's nearly over.

ALL: Yes, Mr Noah.

NOAH: Good. Any problems?

MAN 2: Er, some of us wondered if we might take a little peep at
the plans.

NOAH: Plans for what?

MAN 2: For the, er . . . For what we're making.

NOAH: I've not seen any plans. *(To the* SENIORS*)* Have you
folk seen any plans?

SENIORS: No!

NOAH: You see: no plans! *(Tapping his head)* It's all up here!
Worry not!

MRS NOAH *(off)*: Noah!

NOAH: My boss is calling me!

   Laughter.

NOAH: 'Bye!

ALL: 'Bye, Mr Noah!

   Exit NOAH.

MAN 1: He's not a bad bloke.

KID 5: He's a liar.

ALL: Ooh!

GRANNY 2: Cheeking your elders behind their backs! Mr Noah never lies!

KID 5 *(producing the plans)*: What are these, then?

MAN 4: Well, what are they?

KID 6: We borrowed 'em from Mr Noah's safe.

MAN 4: That's stealing!

GRANNY 1: Put 'em back before you get us all into trouble!

MOST *agree.*

GRANNY 4: What are they, anyway?

KID 5: They're the plans of what we're making.

KID 6: They're the plans that don't exist.

KID 5: So if Noah never had any,

KID 5 ⎫
KID 6 ⎭ : They never can be missed!

Enter SHEM. KID 5 *hides the plans.* SHEM *wanders round, obviously seeking something.*

WOMAN 4: You looking for something, Mr Shem?

SHEM: My dad thinks he might have lost some papers.

WOMAN 1: Not plans, are they?

SHEM: Plans? Oh, no: nothing like that. Well, they're not here. Goodbye.

ALL: Goodbye, Mr Shem!

Exit SHEM.

KID 5: See? They're lying to us.

OLD MAN 2: Why are they?

KID 6: That's for us to find out.

KID 5 *(to MAN 1)*: Here. Take a look at these.

MAN 1: Not me. You're not getting me into trouble.

KID 5 *(to MAN 4)*: Here. You look at 'em.

MAN 4 *(reaching for them, then recoiling)*: No, they're none of my business.

KID 5: Read all about it! Anybody?

ALL *shake their heads.*

KID 5 *(to* KID 6*)*: They don't want to know.

KID 6: Right. We'll play a word-association game.

OLD MAN 1: What's he on about?

OLD MAN 2: Association game.

OLD MAN 1: I'm a Rugby man myself.

Groans.

MAN 3: Shut him up!

KID 6: Welcome to our little game! We'll read a word from Mr
  Noah's non-existent plans, and you say the first word that
  comes into your head. Ready?

ALL: Yes!

KID 6: Bilge.

GRANNY 1: You two!

Laughter.

KID 6: Very witty. Bridge.

GRANNY 2: Cards.

KID 5: Port.

GRANNY 3: Wine.

KID 5: Starboard.

MAN 1: Boats.

KID 6: Scuttle.

GRANNY 4: Coal.

KID 5: Scuppers.

MAN 4: Boats.

KID 6: Lifebuoy.

WOMAN 3: Soap.

KID 5: Anchor.

MAN 2: Boats.

KID 6: Rudder.

OLD MAN 2: Boats.

KID 5: Keel.

KID 2: Canal.

KID 6: Gangplank.

SEVERAL: Boats.
KID 5: Lower deck.
SEVERAL: Boats.
KID 6: Middle deck.
MOST: Boats.
KIDS 5 *and* 6: Maindeck.
ALL: Boats.
OLD MAN 1: Boats!

Laughter.

KID 6: See?
MAN 2: Well, what does that prove?
KID 6: It proves, knucklehead, that we are not building sheds or a barn or a zoo. We're all building a boat!
MAN 2: Five hundred feet long?
KIDS 5 *and* 6: Yes!
MAN 2: Rubbish!
KID 5: Look at these plans, then. If you dare.
MAN 2 *(crossing)*: 'The Ark'. Gangway. Cabins. Galley. You're right: it's a boat. 'One cubit equals five hundred feet.'
KID 3: So what are all these cages we've made?
MAN 2: It says here: 'Mammals. Reptiles. Carnivores.'
GRANNY 1: What's it all mean?
MAN 2: I don't know.
OLD MAN 2: I see what we're making: rigging and sails.

A whistle blows.

WOMAN 3: Back to work.
GRANNY 3: You put those plans back now.
KID 1: But what are we all going to do? They're lying to us! Why are we building a boat up here? And why are they taking animals on it?
WOMAN 1: And why is Mrs Noah buying all the umbrellas she can lay her hands on?
WOMAN 2 And raincoats and wellingtons!
WOMAN 3: Is that true?

WOMAN 4: 'Course it's true! They know something we don't, and they're making damn sure we don't find out, either. These kids are right!

WOMAN 3: I don't care! I'm going back to work: I don't want the sack.

Exit WOMAN 3.

MAN 4: I'll tell you what I think –

WOMAN 3 *shrieks off-stage and re-enters carrying a sack.*

WOMAN 4: She's got the sack.

Laughter.

WOMAN 3: You won't laugh when you see this! Look!

She thrusts the sack at WOMAN 4.

WOMAN 4: There's a letter with it. 'To the finder: Please look after the enclosed, as Mr Noah will not let me take them in the Ark. I do not want them to drown.'

MAN 4: What's in it?

WOMAN 4 *(looking)*: Puppies. All asleep. Miss Rebecca's. I'd better go and hide 'em.

ALL *silently watch her go.*

OLD MAN 1: What's going on? Why aren't we working?

WOMAN 4 *returns without the sack.*

WOMAN 4: They're coming. All of them.

ALL *close ranks as* NOAH *and his* SONS *enter,* HAM *carrying his gun. Silence.*

JAPHETH: Where's my squad of old folks?

The SENIORS *raise their hands.*

GRANNY 4: Here we are!

JAPHETH: Right, come on, folks: let's get cracking! You've had a long break.

GRANNIES 3 *and* 4 *rise.*

KID 5: Sit down, old ladies!

The GRANNIES *hesitate, then sit.*

JAPHETH: I'm their boss! I tell them where to go!
KID 6: And we're telling you where to go.
HAM: You listen to me!
KID 4: No, you listen to us for a change.
HAM: Are you getting back to work?
KIDS: No way!
SHEM: What about my squad? You want your pay, don't you?
ADULTS: Yes.
SHEM: Right, let's move it!

The ADULTS *look at each other and* SOME *rise.*

WOMAN 4: What good is pay when you're drowned?
NOAH: What did you say?
WOMAN 3: You heard.
NOAH: Where do you get this drowning idea?
WOMAN 4 *(handing him the letter)*: From this.
NOAH *(to* JAPHETH*)*: Your wife wrote this! She has no more
    brains than one of her own stupid puppies! I've a good mind to
    let her drown as well!
JAPHETH: Well, I'm staying with her! You won't have enough
    hands to man the Ark, will you? I hope you wreck it! What
    will God say to that?
MAN 2: What has God got to do with all this?
SHEM: You keep out of this! Are you going to work or not?
KID 5: Not till you tell us why we're building a five hundred foot
    boat half-way up a hillside!
HAM: Who says it's a boat?
KID 6: These plans say so!
NOAH: Give them here! *(Snatching them)* Now back to work!
ALL: No!

    RUTH *screams off-stage.* ALL *look. Enter* MRS NOAH,

REBECCA *and* RUTH, *whose hand is bleeding.*

NOAH: Who's done that?

MRS NOAH: You mean, *what's* done it?

SHEM: All right, what's done it?

MRS NOAH: Caging one of our own ferrets has done that, and we're supposed to take two of every animal! (*Waving a list*) Have you men read this list?

HAM: We haven't had time, have we? We can't build a boat as big as the QE2 in our backyard *and* collect thousands of animals. Talk sense.

SARA: Why don't you talk sense? Two rattlesnakes! Two porcupines! Two black mambas! Two king cobras! You've got to be joking!

JAPHETH: Well, we'll all have to suffer a bit . . .

RUTH: Bit is right! It nearly bit my hand off! Bring in the tigers, mate! They might as well chew me to bits! No messing!

MRS NOAH (*indicating the* WORKERS): Why can't some of this lot catch the animals?

NOAH: 'Cause we need 'em to finish the Ark, that's why! I don't know what God's going to say. What do you lads think?

JAPHETH: I say forget most of the animals. They're mostly pests, in any case.

SHEM: Our kid's right, dad. Stick to useful beasts: sheep, goats, cows, ferrets . . .

RUTH: Ferrets! Huh!

HAM: Shut it! (*To* NOAH) This here list is probably just a try-on. God's idea of a joke.

RUTH: Big laugh.

NOAH: All agreed? Finish the Ark and take only useful beasts?

JAPHETH (*raising his hand*): Agreed.

The rest of the NOAH FAMILY *raise their hands and say 'Agreed'.*

NOAH: Eight votes to nil. That's everybody in favour.

WOMAN 2: We haven't voted.

NOAH: Did somebody speak?

WOMAN 1: She did. She said we haven't voted.

MRS NOAH: We don't need to ask you.

WOMAN 1: Why not? Aren't we useful beasts?

HAM: This is our land.

MRS NOAH: Criminals can't vote.

GRANNY 3: Excuse me, are you calling me a criminal, Mrs Noah?

MRS NOAH: Yes. You live on the estate, and estates are one big crime wave. They breed crime.

WOMAN 4: Better than breeding ferrets.

Laughter.

MRS NOAH: What's wrong with ferrets?

OLD MAN 2: Ask your daughter-in-law.

Laughter.

WOMAN 2: And where did you live before you got rich?

NOAH: We've wasted enough time! You're not here to argue and vote: you're here to work! So work or get out!

MAN 1 *(stepping forward)*: Do you mean that? Where would you lot be if we all walked out? You listen to me, Mr Noah. I'm only a common person, and I've been out of work ever since you mechanised your factory. Now, as I understand it, you're making us build this boat so you and your family can watch the rest of us drown. Your missus here talked about a crime wave: well, if that isn't criminal, I don't know what is.

Cheers and applause.

MAN 1: So what is your right to put your class of folk before the rest of us?

More applause and cheering.

HAM *(brandishing his gun)*: This is our right! Might is right! Now on your feet!

33

As the WORKERS *stand, there is a rumble of thunder.* ALL *look up.*

HAM: Hear that! The Lord is brewing up a flood to drown the world! Now work!

KID 6: Just one thing! We could work faster if we could see the plan. Can we use it?

NOAH *looks at his* SONS, *who nod. He gives the plan to* KID 6.

NOAH: Use it properly.

KID 6: We will. *(To* KID 5*)* Would you like to share this?

He tears it in two.

KID 5: Oh, thanks!

SHEM: Stop that!

KIDS 5 *and* 6 *tear their pieces in half and give each half to other* KIDS *who say 'Oh, thanks' as* NOAH'S SONS *try to stop them. The* KIDS *in turn tear their pieces in half and give them to two other people, who say 'Oh, thanks' and repeat the process until all the* WORKERS *have a piece, which they tear up as small as possible while the* NOAH FAMILY *watch helplessly.*

KID 6: You told us to use the plan properly: how about that?

The WORKERS *hold up their pieces of paper.*

NOAH: God gave that plan to us!

NOAH FAMILY: To us! It's ours!

WORKERS: Aw!

KID 5: Oh dear. Let's give 'em their plan back!

The WORKERS *throw pieces of paper over the* FAMILY, *saying 'Whee!'* RUTH *begins to cry again in anger.*

NOAH: Now you've torn it!

Laughter.

NOAH: We can't finish the Ark without the plans!

GRANNY 3: I reckon if God is going to drown all the sinners, Mr Noah, he can drown you as well.

NOAH: What do you mean?

GRANNY 3: I mean your family's all been lying to us. And lying's a sin, isn't it?

There is another rumble of thunder.

HAM *(levelling his gun at KID 5)*: I could kill you! I caught you thieving before, and you stole the plans, didn't you?

KID 5: Yes. And I stole something else as well.

HAM: What?

KID 5: I stole the bullets out of your gun.

Laughter. HAM *squeezes the trigger, exclaims and throws the gun down. More thunder.* MRS NOAH *and* NOAH *sit gloomily.*

MAN 2: How long is this flood going to last?

SARA: Forty days.

MAN 2: What say we all make little rafts?

ALL *glumly shake their heads.*

MAN 3: We'd just starve slowly instead of drowning quickly.

KID 2: Can't we stop the flood?

GRANNY 1: No, the Good Lord sends the weather.

GRANNY 2: None of us can stop it.

Thunder.

MAN 3: It's too late now. *(Holding out a hand)* It's starting to rain.

KID 4: God can stop it! He started it: he can stop it!

KID 3: Right! How does God get in touch with you?

NOAH: Phone.

KID 3: Well, ring him up, now!

MRS NOAH: He's ex-directory.

KID 2: Well, what about the post, or pigeons, or . . .

OLD MAN 1: Prayer.

ALL: What?

OLD MAN 1: Prayer's the way to talk to God.

ALL: Prayer?
OLD MAN 1: You heard me.
OLD MAN 2: I thought you were deaf.
OLD MAN 1: I hear what I want to hear.

   Thunder.

OLD MAN 1: And I can hear that thunder. I reckon God might
   hear us praying.
OLD MAN 2: What shall we say to him?
GRANNY 4: He might like a hymn.
WOMAN 3: We don't sing hymns, do we?
WORKERS: No.
WOMAN 1: I vote we just say we're sorry for our sins. (*To*
   NOAH*)* If I'm allowed to vote now?

   NOAH *nods.*

WOMAN 1: Thank you. *(She looks up.)* Are you listening, God?

   Thunder.

WOMAN 1: Right, he's listening. Tell him we're sorry.

   A FEW *say, 'I'm sorry'.*

WOMAN 1: Come on, all of you: pray! It's your last chance!

   Gradually, one by one, ALL *begin to pray, saying, 'I'm sorry.'*
   The prayer builds in a crescendo as thunder rumbles. The phone rings.
   Silence. ALL *stare at the phone. It rings again.*

MRS NOAH: Well, answer it!
NOAH *(at the phone)*: Hello. Yes. Yes. No. Yes. That's all right.

   He puts the phone down.

MRS NOAH: Well?
NOAH: Wrong number.

   ALL *groan. Lightning and thunder.* REBECCA *starts to cry.*

WOMAN 1: Crying won't help. Come on: pray again! Louder!

ALL *begin praying, even louder. Lightning and thunder. The phone rings again, but they are praying so loud, mostly with their eyes closed, that only* OLD MAN 1 *hears it. He goes to the phone, and those who notice him say 'Shh!' The praying subsides.*

OLD MAN 1: Hello. Yes. Yes. No. Yes. That's all right. And you have a nice day, too.

ALL: Well?

OLD MAN 1: It's all right.

NOAH: Was it God?

OLD MAN 1: Well, he said he was. Booming voice.

NOAH: That's him.

MAN 3: Hey, the rain's stopped.

ALL: Aw!

A final low rumble of thunder.

MRS NOAH: What did he say?

OLD MAN 1: Who?

ALL: God!

OLD MAN 1: Oh, God. Well, he says he's postponing the flood.

Cheers.

OLD MAN 1: He says he's putting us all on probation for a year, and he wants to see more working together and less crime. Oh, and he reckons that the Ark will make into a good Temple.

ALL *begin to chatter.* OLD MAN 1 *gestures for silence.* ALL *shush each other.*

OLD MAN 1: And he says we've all to shake hands with people we don't know and say, 'Have a nice day.'

As ALL *go round quietly and happily greeting each other, music begins. It could be the theme from the last movement of Beethoven's Pastoral Symphony. The phone rings again.* MRS NOAH *picks it up with a smile.*

MRS NOAH: Mrs Noah speaking. Oh yes, we're all very happy!

Just one more thing, is there? What's that, sir? *(Her smile disappears.)* Yes, I'll tell them. Goodbye.

NOAH: Was it God again?

She nods.

NOAH: Something wrong?

She nods.

KID 6: What is it, Mrs Noah?

MRS NOAH: God says . . . he wants his plans back.

ALL *(surveying the pieces of paper)*: Oh, no!

[*Curtain.*]

THE MYSTERY GIFT

by BILL TORDOFF and DAVID DOUGHAN

CHARACTERS

Greeks
KING AGAMEMNON, *an old man*
ULYSSES, *a general*
SERGEANT
SOLDIER 1
SOLDIER 2, *the youngest*
SOLDIER 3
SOLDIER 4
SOLDIER 5
SIMPLEX, *a simple soldier*

Trojans
KING PRIAM
AENEAS, *a general*
OFFICER
FIRST SENTRY (JASON)
SECOND SENTRY (PHIL)
IRIS, *Jason's wife*
PHOEBE, *Phil's wife*
FLORA ⎫
JUNO ⎬ *Phil's sisters*
SYBIL ⎭

CASSANDRA, *Priam's daughter, a prophetess*
FIRST HANDMAID ⎱ *attendants on Cassandra*
SECOND HANDMAID ⎰
MOIRA
DORIS
FIRST PRIESTESS, (*the eldest*)
SECOND PRIESTESS
THIRD PRIESTESS
FOURTH PRIESTESS
FIFTH PRIESTESS (CHLOE, *the youngest*)
SMALLEST TROJAN

SCENE 1: The Greek camp, outside the walls of Troy
SCENE 2: On the walls of Troy
SCENE 3: Outside the walls
SCENE 4: Troy: the temple of Diana

The events of the play take place in Troy in Asia Minor

Note on the Horse
The Horse need only be a cut-out, and should not be realistic. (The Trojans do not even recognise it as a horse.) Its jaw needs to be hinged, and there should be a structure behind it on which actors climb in and out. (The gap between the legs need not be cut out.) If you have a traverse-curtain, the horse can be set in position before the play starts, and the curtains pulled back far enough to reveal it at the beginning of Scene 3. Otherwise it can be pushed on with its rear masked by a wing curtain.

Properties
Drink and food, including a cake and a bottle (Phil's SISTERS)
Hammer (SIMPLEX)
Scroll (AGAMEMNON)
Letter (On Horse)
Knitting (PRIESTESS 1)
Book (PHIL, second sentry)

Bags of loot (TROJANS)
Placard (Inside Horse)

Sound Effects
Cock-crow
Hammering
Gong
Sirens, bells, etc.

Scene 1

The Greek Camp. SOLDIER 1 *is leaning on his spear looking bored. He sees the audience, comes forward and speaks.*

SOLDIER 1: Little poem:

There was once a lad called Paris,
A prince in a town called Troy, (*Gesturing*)
3,000 years before you were born,
A spoiled but handsome boy.

In his father's eyes he could do no wrong,
And what Paris asked for he got.
And the year he was named as the heir to the throne
His Daddy gave Paris a yacht.

He sailed the seas till he came to Greece,
And his sails he'd scarcely furled
When the Greeks said 'Welcome to town, sit yourself
    down:
We'd like you to judge Miss World.'

So Paris said 'Who do you fancy?'
And the Greeks said 'Ah, that'd be tellin',
But if you're looking for clues it said on the news
That the bookies have laid odds on Helen.'

And once Helen walked on that platform
The other girls didn't have a prayer,
For she was the loveliest lass in the world:
A dream with the sun in her hair.

So Paris crowned Helen and gave her a kiss,
And said as she giggled with joy:
'Come down the harbour: I'll show you my yacht.'
And she did. And they sailed off to Troy.

Her husband was Prince of the Spartans,
And he swore and he raged and he foamed.
Till all of the other princes of Greece
Vowed to help him to bring Helen home.

They called thousands of men to their colours,
A thousand keels lay on the slips.
And soon the men were in fighting trim
And their fleet was a thousand ships.

The Trojans had heard we were coming
And they laboured for months without break
To make Troy town a fortress strong
That we Greeks could never take.

Our warships crashed onto the beach:
We launched a fierce attack.
We fought with pride and thousands died,
But the Trojans threw us back.

For ten long years we've fought this war,
Each year more soldiers die.
And still above those city walls
The Trojan banners fly.

SERGEANT *(off)*: You there! Straighten up! *(Enter SERGEANT.)* At ease, soldier! Heard anything?

SOLDIER 1: No, sergeant: just the shouting.

SERGEANT: Same here. It's got me worried. It should be over by now and we should have won.

SOLDIER 1: Somebody's coming now!

SOLDIER 4 *staggers in. They support him.*

SERGEANT: Well, what happened?

SOLDIER 4: Result. *(Pants)* Greeks 4. *(Pants)* Trojans *(Pants)* 5, after extra time.

SOLDIER 1: Greeks 4, Trojans 5! We've lost again!

SERGEANT: And that's the third time on the trot that the
Trojans have won the cup! Know what that means?

SOLDIER 1: What?

SOLDIER 4: No drinks tonight.

SOLDIER 1: Why not?

SERGEANT: You know why: 'cause there's only two cups, and
the Trojans have won 'em both.

SOLDIER 4: Yes, they won the League Championship Cup last
month.

SOLDIER 1: We were runners–up, though.

SOLDIER 4: Yes, 'cause there's only two teams in the league,
aren't there?

SERGEANT: Here they come.

Enter GREEK SOLDIERS 2, 3 *and* 5 *wearing football scarves and
looking depressed.*

SOLDIER 2: Have you heard?

SERGEANT: 5–4 to them.

SOLDIERS *nod.*

SOLDIER 3: We were winning 4–3 with two minutes to go, then
Achilles tripped over his spear and gave the ball away and they
scored.

SOLDIER 4: They shouldn't have to carry spears in the Cup Final.

SOLDIER 3: Trojans keep altering the rules.

SOLDIER 2: I couldn't see half of the game with that fat woman
in that posh dress standing in front of me. Eating cream cakes all
the time, and us half-starved.

SOLDIER 5: Don't you know who that was?

SOLDIER 2: Some Trojan broad.

SOLDIER 5: That fat woman is Greek. That is Princess Helen.

SOLDIER 2: You're lying! I saw a picture of Helen, just before
we came out here. She's beautiful and slim.

SOLDIER 5: She was ten years ago, but all those cream cakes have
built up the blubber. Helen's a heavyweight now.

SOLDIER 2: And we've had to join the army just to get that fat woman back to Greece!

SOLDIER 3: Yes, if we got her on the boat now she'd sink it.

TROJANS *(off)*: We've won the cup! We've won the cup!

SOLDIERS: Belt up, Trojans!

TROJANS *(off)*: We're off to have a drink! We're off to have a drink!

SOLDIERS: Get lost!

TROJANS *(off)*: Greeks are weak! Greeks are weak! Bye-bye, Greeks, bye-bye!

ALL *look depressed.*

SOLDIER 2: Perhaps we'll win next year.

SOLDIER 4: No chance. The Trojans all eat properly, they live in warm houses, they get regular leave.

SOLDIER 3: And look at us. We have to live in leaky tents, and half our food-ships get sunk.

SOLDIER 1: Trojans beat us at everything: football, fighting, athletics, the lot.

SOLDIER 3: I suppose we've just got to soldier on.

ALL: Mmm.

SOLDIER 5: Why? Why should we soldier on?

SOLDIER 2: What else can we do?

SOLDIER 5: We can cut our losses and sail back home.

SOLDIER 3: The officers'll stop us.

SOLDIER 5: How can they? There's ten men to every officer. Besides, I bet most of 'em are as fed up as we are. I know the sergeant here is.

SOLDIER 4: Who's in favour of going back home to Greece then?

ALL *raise their hands.*

SOLDIER 4: Against? None. Right: we're going home.

ALL *(singing)*: We want to go home,

We want to go home.

We don't want to go in the trenches no more,

We're going back to our Hellenic shore.
We're going to go over the sea
Where the Trojans they can't get at we.
Oh, my, we're not going to die,
We're going to go home.

SOLDIER 1: Officers! It's the King and Ulysses!

Enter AGAMEMNON and ULYSSES.

SERGEANT: Attention!

The SOLDIERS stand reluctantly to attention.

SERGEANT: Three cheers for King Agamemnon!

ALL cheer feebly.

AGAMEMNON: Thank you, men. What was the singing?
Another victory for our chaps, was it?

ULYSSES: No, I'm afraid our team lost again, your Majesty.

AGAMEMNON: Well, it's only a game. Perhaps we'll win next
year, or the year after that. Thank you, Sergeant.

AGAMEMNON and ULYSSES start to go.

SERGEANT: Sir! Your Majesty!

AGAMEMNON: Yes?

SERGEANT: Some of the men were wondering if we could go
home, sir, instead of staying here.

AGAMEMNON: But we must stay here to, er ... Why must we
stay here, Ulysses?

ULYSSES: To rescue Princess Helen, your Majesty.

AGAMEMNON: That's right, to rescue Princess Helen. So you
don't *really* want to go home, do you?

ALL: Oh yes, we do!

AGAMEMNON: Oh. But why?

SOLDIER 5: When we first came here, sir, you said we were
going to capture Troy, get Princess Helen back, grab some loot
and sail straight home. Didn't he, lads?

ALL: Yes, he did!

SOLDIER 3: Back in six months, you said!

ALL: Yes!

ULYSSES: Look, men, I admit the war hasn't turned out exactly as we planned it . . .

SOLDIER 1: It certainly hasn't!

ULYSSES: But we've done our best to capture Troy.

SOLDIER 3: Well, our best isn't good enough, sir. We can't even beat the Trojans at football, so what chance have we of getting into the city?

SOLDIER 5: Anyway, that doesn't matter now, because we don't want to get *into* Troy: we want to get out of here, fast! Right, lads?

SOLDIERS: Right!

SOLDIER 1: Right, we're going home, and no messing.

SOLDIER 4 *(singing)*: I want to go home . . .

ULYSSES: Now look, men, let's not be hasty . . .

SOLDIER 3: Hasty? After ten years!

SOLDIERS: Yeah!

ULYSSES: Can we give it one more try? Just one more effort? If it doesn't work this time, we'll go back.

SOLDIER 1: Well, how about it, lads?

ALL *look doubtful.*

SOLDIER 2: Well, if it's just one more . . .

SOLDIER 3: I suppose so.

SOLDIER 4: Only once more, though.

SERGEANT: All in favour of one last try?

ALL *grudgingly raise their hands.*

ULYSSES: Good men! So that's settled!

SERGEANT: Oh no it's not, sir. How are we going to get into Troy?

ULYSSES: Ah! Good thinking! Well, we have some of the best brains in the army here, and I'm sure we can think of something between us. Any suggestions?

ALL *think*.

AGAMEMNON: We seem to have tried every possible way.

ALL *nod*.

SOLDIER 3: Yes, we've run out of ideas.
SOLDIER 2: There must be thousands of ways.
ALL: Such as?
SOLDIER 2: How about battering rams?
ALL: We've tried it.
SOLDIER 2: Or catapults.
ALL: Tried it.
SOLDIER 2: Mining under the walls.
ALL: Tried it.
SOLDIER 2: Starving 'em out.
ALL: Tried it.

Pause.

SOLDIER 2: Ah! What about diverting the . . .
ALL: Tried it.
SOLDIER 2: Oh.
SERGEANT: You're right, your Majesty. We've tried every
    possible way.
ULYSSES: I know! You know what our trouble is? We're all
    sensible men, and we've all had sensible ideas, but sensible ideas
    don't work. So what we want is a stupid idea. Who is the
    stupidest, most brainless soldier in your section?
ALL: Simplex, sir.
ULYSSES: Who?
SOLDIER 3: Simplex, sir.
SERGEANT: Ah, he's just over there, sir. Simplex! Come over
    here at the double! Left, right! No, left. Left! Oh, never mind:
    just come.

Enter SIMPLEX.

AGAMEMNON: Now, private, your name is Simplex?

SIMPLEX: Erm, yeah.

AGAMEMNON: We want your advice.

SIMPLEX: What?

ULYSSES: You. We want you to help us.

SIMPLEX: Aw, me?

ULYSSES: Yes. Now, if you wanted to get into Troy, what would you do?

SIMPLEX: Troy.

ALL: Troy.

SIMPLEX *(thinking, then)*: If I wanted to get into Troy, I would knock on the gate and say 'Hello, Troy people, could I come in, please?

> *Laughter.*

AGAMEMNON: That gate is locked and barred and barricaded. They won't let us in: they hate us.

SIMPLEX: Aw, I wondered about that.

ULYSSES: Come on, laddie, think again.

SIMPLEX: Right, sir.

> *He thinks,* ALL *watching.*

SIMPLEX: Er . . .

> ALL *look hopeful.*

SIMPLEX: No.

> *He thinks again.*

SIMPLEX: Aw, yeah! If I wanted to get into Troy, I'd build a great big box. A wood box. Make it like, say, a horse. And, er, put a lot of our soldiers into it, and, er, go away and leave it where the Troy people'd see it. Then they'd come out and say, 'Oh, what a lovely horse!' and they'd take it into Troy. Then our men could get out and open the gates and the rest of our men could get in!

> *He has become excited, and looks round smiling hopefully. There is*

a great burst of laughter from ALL *except* ULYSSES, *who looks thoughtful.*

ULYSSES: Thank you, Simplex. Off you go.
SIMPLEX: Aw, thank *you*, sir.

   Exit SIMPLEX.

SOLDIER 1: Well, you wanted a stupid idea, sir, and you got one.
ULYSSES: Yes, it's a stupid, brainless, idiotic plan.
ALL: Hear, hear!
ULYSSES: And it might just work.
ALL: What?
ULYSSES: I said it might just work. If it does, we go home. And
   if it doesn't, we go home. Right?
ALL: Right!
ULYSSES: So, let's get working. Intelligence can design the horse,
   Engineers can make it, Artillery can supply a chassis and Cavalry
   can pose as models. And everyone else can get ready to set sail!
ALL *(singing)*: We're going to go home,
                 We're going to go home.
                 We don't have to go in the trenches no more,
                 We're going back to our Hellenic shore.
                 We're going to go over the sea
                 Where the Trojans they can't get at we.
                 Oh, my, we're not going to die,
                 We're going to go home.

   ALL *go out singing.*

Scene 2

On the walls of Troy. A cock crows. Enter JASON *and* PHIL, *Trojan sentries, one from each side.* PHIL *wears a Troy United scarf.*

JASON: Halt in the name of Troy! Who goes there?
PHIL: Aw, come off it, Jason. You know it's me: it always is.

JASON: Rules are rules, Phil. What's today's password?

PHIL: Aw, hang about, I can't think.

JASON: The password is 'Troy' and the counter-sign is 'United'.
  You should remember: they're your team.

PHIL: Aw, right. *(Advancing)* Troy!

JASON *(Advancing)*: United! Correct.

  They relax.

JASON: I wonder who won the match?

PHIL: I wish I knew. Sorry about forgetting the password. It's all
  that noise from the Greeks down there that puts me off.

JASON: Yes. I wonder what they've been up to?

PHIL: Anybody's guess. I hope they're not going to attack.

  They peer out over the audience.

JASON: All that banging and shouting all night.

PHIL: Officer!

  They spring to attention. Enter OFFICER.

OFFICER: Good morning, men.

JASON: Password, sir?

OFFICER: Troy!

PHIL: United!

JASON: Correct, sir.

OFFICER: Why are you wearing that scarf with your uniform,
  private?

PHIL: Aw, sorry, sir, but it was the Cup Final yesterday, and I've
  followed United ever since I was little. Can you tell us who
  won, sir? We've been out here on duty all the time.

OFFICER: Er, it was either Greek Spartans or Troy United. No,
  can't remember. Sorry! Now, anything to report?

JASON: Yes, sir. Them Greeks have been making a lot of noises
  during the night.

OFFICER: What sort of noises? Rude noises?

JASON: No, sir. Banging and shouting.

PHIL: And hammering and sawing, sir. We thought we ought to tell you, sir.

OFFICER: Quite right. They're strange people, these Greeks. Keep your eyes open! All right, men: carry on!

Exit OFFICER. SENTRIES *relax.*

IRIS *(off)*: Yoo-hoo! *(Peering on)* Has your officer gone, Jason?

JASON: Hello, love! Yes, he's gone. This is a surprise! What are you doing all this way from home?

Enter IRIS.

IRIS: And I've brought a surprise for Phil as well: your wife!

Enter PHOEBE.

IRIS: And all your sisters!

Enter FLORA, JUNO, *and* SYBIL, *waving Troy United scarves.*

SISTERS: Ta-dah!

PHIL: Who won?

SISTERS: We did! 5–4 after extra time!

PHIL: Aw, great!

ALL *(singing. Tune: 'Cwm Rhondda')*:

> We all follow Troy United,
> They're the best team in the land.
> Greeks are weak and so are Persians,
> All Egyptians should be banned.
> Troy United! Troy United!
> We'll support you evermore!
> We'll support you evermore!

ALL *cheer.*

SYBIL: And to celebrate we've made you a cake in United colours!

JUNO: And we've brought a few bottles!

SYBIL: So let's have a party!

PHIL: What? Now?

PHOEBE: Why not? Your officer won't be back for an hour, will he?

They begin to unpack.

JASON: Look out! He's coming back!

The WOMEN *exclaim, grab the food and drink and rush off, leaving one bottle which* PHIL *snatches and holds behind his back as the* OFFICER *enters.*

OFFICER: Troy!

PHIL: 5–4, sir, after extra time!

OFFICER: What?

JASON: He means 'United', sir.

PHIL: I mean 'United', sir.

OFFICER: Good. Good. I came back to ask if you'd heard any more strange noises just now?

JASON: No, sir.

PHIL: Nothing at all, sir.

OFFICER: That's odd. I could have sworn I heard singing in weird, high-pitched voices.

One of the WOMEN *giggles off-stage.*

OFFICER: Listen! Did you hear that?

PHIL: There wasn't anything, sir.

JASON: It's the loneliness out here, sir. We're all starting to hear things.

OFFICER: You could be right.

He strolls round the SENTRIES. PHIL *turns to keep the bottle hidden.*

OFFICER: I know life's tough in this lonely outpost, miles from your wives and families, with poor food and nothing to drink.

He starts to go. The SENTRIES *begin to relax. He suddenly turns.*

OFFICER: I know! I'll send two of the others to relieve you for a spell.

JASON: No, sir: please don't do that!

PHIL: We're happy to be here defending our beloved country, sir!

OFFICER: Well done! Spoken like true sons of Troy! Carry on!

BOTH *(saluting)*: Sir!

> *Exit* OFFICER. JASON *follows to make sure he has gone.*
> FLORA *peeps on.*

FLORA: Can we come back?

JASON: Yes, he's gone.

> *The* WOMEN *re-enter.*

FLORA: Right, let's have a good time!

> *They start to unpack again.*

CASSANDRA: *(off, loud)*: Woe!!

HANDMAIDS *(off, feebler)*: Woe!

PHOEBE: What the heck's that?

IRIS: Oh, no! Just when we were going to have a bit of fun!

JUNO: Well, who is it?

IRIS: It's that Princess Cassandra. She's a right Moaning Minnie.

FLORA: She is. If her dad wasn't the King, she'd have been locked up.

JUNO: Oh, I've heard about her. Isn't she some sort of fortune-teller?

FLORA: She calls herself a prophetess. I know what I call her.

IRIS: She's here!

> *Enter* CASSANDRA *with her* HANDMAIDS *behind her. The* WOMEN *curtsey, but she ignores them.*

CASSANDRA: Woe! The doom of Troy is nigh!

HANDMAIDS: Doom is nigh!

SYBIL: Who are the other two?

IRIS: They're her handmaids. They have to follow wherever she goes and chant all that rubbish.

SYBIL: What a rotten job!

CASSANDRA: Woe unto the city of Troy!

HANDMAIDS: Woe to Troy!

CASSANDRA: For I foresee death, destruction and woe!

HANDMAIDS: Destruction and woe!

CASSANDRA: Doom is certain. Soon we will perish and end in woe!

HANDMAIDS: End in woe!

SYBIL: Charming!

PHOEBE: Excuse me, miss. Is it true that you can tell everything that's going to happen?

CASSANDRA: Yea, alas: 'tis all woe!

HANDMAIDS: 'Tis all . . .

PHOEBE: All right: I heard her the first time! (*To* CASSANDRA) No, I just wondered, could you tell me what sort of weather we're going to have today, 'cause if it's fine I'd like to do some washing.

CASSANDRA: Weather forecast for the Eastern Mediterranean. Egypt: starting cloudy, with a few scattered plagues of frogs, flies, boils and locusts; some death of first-born later in the day. Sodom and Gomorrah: overcast, changing to rains of fire and brimstone. Troy and surrounding areas: starting fine but changing to woe!

HANDMAIDS: Changing to woe!

IRIS: Can't she say anything except woe?

CASSANDRA: Yes. Alas.

HANDMAIDS: Alas!

CASSANDRA: For see yonder! (*Pointing*) Observe! Look!

HANDMAIDS (*pointing*): Observe! Look!

JASON: Look at what? What are they pointing at?

PHIL: Nothing.

JASON: What are they pointing at it for then?

CASSANDRA: Fools! What was there yesterday?

HANDMAIDS: There yesterday.

PHIL: Well, er, nothing except the Greek camp.

JASON: That's it! They've gone! The Greeks have gone!

ALL *cheer.*

JASON: That's what the noise was during the night! Run and tell the officer!

Exit PHIL.

JASON: Let's clear up. We'll have the party when we come off duty.

IRIS: Hang on. *(Pointing out over another part of the audience)* Look at that!

JASON: Blimey, what is it?

SYBIL: Looks like a packing-case on stilts.

FLORA: I don't like it.

JUNO: Oh, forget it! Let's go and tell everybody that the Greeks have gone.

They start to go off.

CASSANDRA: Stop! I know what it is!

HANDMAIDS: It is!

JUNO: I think we can guess, but tell us.

CASSANDRA: 'Tis woe!

HANDMAIDS: Woe!

JUNO: I thought it might be.

CASSANDRA *exits moaning 'Woe! Woe! Woe!' The* HANDMAIDS *shrug apologetically and hurry after her, repeating 'Woe!' The* OTHERS *stand mimicking* CASSANDRA, *then burst out laughing.*

IRIS: Come on, everybody: let's spread the good news!

ALL *go out, chattering and laughing.*

Scene 3

The sound of hammering. SIMPLEX *is finishing the horse, watched by* ULYSSES *and* AGAMEMNON.

SIMPLEX *(standing back)*: There! It's finished! What do you think of it, your Majesty?

AGAMEMNON: It's er . . . very original.

SIMPLEX: Oh, thank you, your Majesty.

ULYSSES: How many men will it hold, Simplex?

SIMPLEX: Er, about seven. Six at a squeeze.

AGAMEMNON: Is that enough?

ULYSSES: Just about, sir. Here they come.

SERGEANT *(off)*: Left, right! Left, right!

    Enter SERGEANT *and* GREEK SOLDIERS.

SERGEANT: Squad, halt! Special Service Group all present and correct, your Majesty!

AGAMEMNON: Mm. A fine body of men. *(Producing a large scroll)* I'll just make a little speech . . .

ULYSSES: I'll read it to them inside the horse, sir. We must get inside before the Trojans wake up. Any problems, men?

SOLDIER: I'm getting a cold, sir. I keep sneezing.

ULYSSES: Too late to worry about that. Get aboard!

    The SOLDIERS *climb into the horse.*

ULYSSES: So you sail round the headland with the rest of the army, sir, and sneak back after dark. We'll open the city gates for you.

AGAMEMNON: How can we be sure that the enemy will take the horse inside?

ULYSSES: Don't worry, sir: Simplex has arranged that.

    He climbs up.

ULYSSES: Simplex! Cover the trapdoor. Goodbye, sir. See you tomorrow night.

He disappears. SIMPLEX *throws a cloth over the horse's back. There is a cheer from the* TROJANS *offstage.*

SIMPLEX: The Troy people are coming, sir! Hurry!

SIMPLEX *and* AGAMEMNON *hurry out. There is a pause, then a crowd of* TROJANS *enter. At first they do not see the horse, but stare out over the audience.*

SMALLEST: There they go: sailing away! Good riddance to Greek rubbish!

ALL *cheer and leap about. Seeing the horse,* ALL *except* MOIRA *and* DORIS *fall silent and examine it.*

MOIRA: Oo, isn't it lovely to be outside the city walls? I just can't believe there aren't any Greeks around any more.

SMALLEST: What do you make of this great big article, then?

MOIRA: Ee, I don't know. Where's it come from?

SMALLEST: Them Greeks left it.

DORIS: Just looks like a box with a stick at each corner and a lump on the end.

MOIRA: Modern art, I suppose.

AENEAS *(entering)*: Make way for the King! Make way for King Priam and Princess Cassandra!

Enter PHIL *and* JASON, *who move back the crowd, followed by* PRIAM, CASSANDRA *and the* HANDMAIDS.

AENEAS: Three cheers for the King! Hip, hip!

ALL *cheer.*

PRIAM: Thank you, my people. What's this strange object, Aeneas?

AENEAS: It's a mystery, sir. First the Greeks sail away after ten years – just like that – then they leave this great ugly thing. I can't understand it.

CASSANDRA: I understand it!

IRIS: We all know what you make of it: woe!

CROWD: Woe!
AENEAS: But what is it?
IRIS: It's supposed to be an animal, isn't it?

Murmurs of agreement.

PHOEBE: Could be. Those sticks could be its legs.
FLORA: Right, and that's its head.
AENEAS: I believe you're right, but what sort of animal?
PHIL: It's a pig, is that sir. An insult from the Greeks. We should
  burn it.

Some of the CROWD *agree.*

JASON: That's not a pig: its neck's too long. It's a dog, is that.
DORIS: It still looks like a box to me.
JASON: Well, it's a boxer dog, then.
CROWD *(jeering)*: Ugh!
PHIL: Pig or dog, it doesn't matter. It's still a Greek insult!

The CROWD *agree.*

DORIS *(who has been inspecting the horse)*: Wait a minute! There's a
  letter stuck on it.
PRIAM: Well done! Read it, Aeneas.
AENEAS: Very good, sir. *(Reading)* 'Dear Trojans. As we do not
  seem to have got anywhere much these past ten years, we have
  decided to jack it in and go back home to Greece. We could not
  get everything on the boat, so have left you a mystery gift,
  hoping it will come in handy. Sorry if we have caused you any
  inconvenience by besieging you. Goodbye and good luck. Yours
  sincerely, Greeks. P.S. It is a horse.'
SMALLEST: That thing, a horse?

ALL laugh.

JUNO: You must admit, it's very nice of them to think of us like
  that.

Murmurs of agreement.

PRIAM: Well, what can we do with it? Any suggestions?
AENEAS: War memorial, sir.
SYBIL: Be nice in a children's playground, your Majesty.
IRIS: No! After what the Greeks have done to us, I say have nothing to do with it!
SMALLEST: Hear, hear!
PHOEBE: Let's smash it up!
SYBIL: Chop it to bits!
DORIS: Set fire to it!
MOIRA: Dirty Greek rubbish!
CROWD: Yeah!

> The SOLDIERS *try to hold back the* CROWD *as they advance on the horse.*

HORSE *(its lips moving)*: Take me to the temple of Diana.
CROWD *(recoiling)*: Oh!
JUNO: Its lips moved!
DORIS: It spoke!
AGAMEMNON: What do they say?
AENEAS: The horse, sir: it spoke!
AGAMEMNON: What did it say?
HORSE: Take me to the temple of Diana.
AGAMEMNON: Amazing. Do you people still want to destroy it?
FLORA: No, your Majesty. It's a magic horse, is that.

> *Murmurs of agreement.*

JUNO: I vote we take it to the temple, like it says.
MOIRA: Hear, hear! It'll bring us good luck.
AGAMEMNON: All in favour of taking it into the temple?

> ALL *raise their hands except* CASSANDRA. *Her* HANDMAIDS *lower theirs.*

SYBIL: It's a talking magic horse.
CASSANDRA: Fools! It's not magic! There's someone hidden inside it!

There is a sneeze from inside the HORSE.

HANDMAIDS: Someone inside it!

ALL *lower their hands and look at the horse.*

AGAMEMNON: People mock Cassandra, but she's very often right.

AENEAS: I'll test it, your Majesty: I have some experience in magic.

He approaches the horse.

AENEAS: Is there anybody there? One rap for yes, two for no.

A loud rap from inside the horse. ALL *look tense. Then another:* ALL *relax and smile.*

AENEAS: No one inside, your Majesty.

ALL *cheer.*

AGAMEMNON: Take the Greek gift into the temple of Diana. May it bring good luck to Troy!

The CROWD *cheer.* AGAMEMNON *and* AENEAS *go out.*

OFFICER: Everybody bring ropes!
CASSANDRA: Wait!
HANDMAIDS: Wait!
CASSANDRA: I warn you!
HANDMAIDS: Warn you!
CASSANDRA: If that thing enters our city, we shall have nothing but . . .
CROWD: Woe! Woe! Woe!
SMALLEST: Whoa, horsey!

The CROWD *laugh.*

PHOEBE: Come and get your washing lines, girls, and leave old Moaning Minnie!

The CROWD *go out, chattering.* CASSANDRA *and* HANDMAIDS *go out the other side. The* HORSE *laughs.*

Scene 4

*The temple of Diana. The scene is empty except for the horse and a
bench in front of it. A Greek head slowly emerges from the opening in
the horse. A gong sounds and the head ducks back. Enter four bored*
PRIESTESSES, *who line up in front of the horse, facing the audience.*
PRIESTESS 2 *yawns. The gong sounds again.*

PRIESTESS 1: O Diana, keep us pure.
ALL: O Diana, keep us pure.

> *They sit and relax.* PRIESTESS 1 *takes out her knitting.*

PRIESTESS 1: Ooh, I hate overtime in this temple.
PRIESTESS 2: Yes, it's spooky. Who'd be a priestess?
PRIESTESS 4: Well, it's a job.
PRIESTESS 3: Right. Hey, where's that new girl?
PRIESTESS 1: Young Chloe? Isn't she here? She asked me if she
    could tell her mother she had to work late, but I saw her outside
    talking to a young soldier.
PRIESTESS 2: They're all alike, these youngsters: they think being
    a priestess is easy till they try it.
PRIESTESS 3: She's coming.

> *Enter* PRIESTESS 5 (CHLOE). *She wears heavy make-up and a
> more revealing dress than the others. She is chewing.*

PRIESTESS 5: Oh, you're all here. What do I have to do now?
PRIESTESS 4: Come and sit here, love. When the gong sounds,
    we all stand up and say, 'O Diana, keep us pure.'
PRIESTESS 5: Sounds like fun. I'd rather be rich.
PRIESTESS 4: Not 'poor': '*pure*'. 'O Diana, keep us *pure.*'
PRIESTESS 5: Aw. I don't know what 'Keep us pure' means.
PRIESTESS 1: I can believe that.
PRIESTESS 3: All the same, why are we working over?
PRIESTESS 4: Guarding this thing, aren't we?
PRIESTESS 3: Well, why us?

PRIESTESS 1: Because this horse had to be brought into our temple, so we have to guard it.

PRIESTESS 5: Horse? Is that what it's supposed to be?

PRIESTESS 3: So they say.

PRIESTESS 1: On your feet, girls: time for the next bong.

They sigh and stand wearily. The gong sounds.

ALL: O Diana, keep us pure.

They sit.

PRIESTESS 5: What are you knitting, eh?

PRIESTESS 1: Nothing to do with you, young lady.

PRIESTESS 5: All right, I only asked.

She stands and looks at the horse.

PRIESTESS 5: Why don't you knit a new blanket for the horse? Hey, let's go horse-riding!

She clambers up on the horse.

PRIESTESS 1: Come down off there! It's sacred, that thing.

PRIESTESS 5: No, it's fun! Coming down the straight now and they're neck and neck, nothing in it. Now it's Wooden Horse coming up on the inside, making a late challenge. Come on, Wooden Horse!

PRIESTESS 2: Take no notice of her: perhaps she'll go away. What *are* you knitting?

PRIESTESS 1: My sister-in-law's expecting.

PRIESTESS 2: Again?

PRIESTESS 1: Mm.

PRIESTESS 5 *is inspecting the horse's back.*

PRIESTESS 3: Hey, did you hear what Hecuba said to Helen the other day?

PRIESTESSES: No, what did Hecuba say to Helen the other day?

They laugh.

PRIESTESS 3: Well, Helen said she'd go back home unless we fed her better . . .

There is a loud sneeze from the HORSE.

PRIESTESS 4: Bless you.
PRIESTESS 3: Don't mention it. Anyway, Hecuba says . . .
PRIESTESS 5: Hey, there's an opening in the horse up here!
PRIESTESS 1: Take no notice of her. What were you saying?
PRIESTESS 3: Yes, Hecuba says, 'Why don't you go back to Greece? You eat like a horse.'

ALL *laugh*.

PRIESTESS 5: Hey, it's opening! It's full of . . .

She disappears.

PRIESTESS 5 (*off*): Oh! Ooh!
PRIESTESS 3: 'And there might be a few more cream cakes left for the rest of us.'
PRIESTESSES: She never!
PRIESTESS 3: She did!
PRIESTESS 1: Nearly time for a bong.

They stand. The gong sounds.

PRIESTESSES: O Diana, keep us pure.

They sit and relax.

PRIESTESS 1: Just one more bong to go.
PRIESTESS 4: Hey, where's young Chloe?
PRIESTESS 1: She was up on the horse a minute ago. (*Standing and looking*) Chloe!
PRIESTESS 2: She'll have gone off again somewhere.

PRIESTESS 1 *sits.*

PRIESTESS 3: She doesn't seem to realise there's openings in this job.
PRIESTESS 2: Yes. All she can think about is looking for soldiers.

PRIESTESS 1: Well, she's looking in the wrong place here.

They laugh.

PRIESTESS 3: Time for the last bong.

They stand expectantly. The gong sounds.

PRIESTESSES *(gabbling)*: O–Diana–keep–us–pure!
PRIESTESS 1: Right, that's it, girls. No more overtime this week. Goodbye, horse.

The PRIESTESSES *hurry out. Pause. A head appears from the horse. There is the sound of the* OFFICER'S *voice and marching. The head pops back. Enter* OFFICER, PHIL *and* JASON.

OFFICER: Left, right! Left, right! Halt! Right turn! Stand at ease! Now, you men, keep a close guard on this object. Don't let anybody take it away, don't let anybody near it. Any questions? Right! Attention!

He marches off. Pause. They relax. PHIL *takes out a book. They nod at each other.*

JASON: Right!

They turn and march out in opposite directions, PHIL *reading. A head peers from the horse, but disappears as the* SENTRIES *return. They halt, turn and march off again.* GREEK SOLDIER 1 *gets out of the horse and follows* JASON. *We hear a blow, a cry, then* PHIL, *still reading, and* SOLDIER 1 *re-enter, with* SOLDIER 1 *wearing* JASON's *cloak. They halt, turn and march off. As they do so,* SOLDIER 2 *climbs out and follows* SOLDIER 1. *We hear another blow and cry.*

SOLDIER 1 *(off)*: It's me, you fool!
SOLDIER 2: *(off)*: Sorry!

Re-enter PHIL *and* SOLDIERS 1 *and* 2, *with* 2 *hiding behind* 1. *They halt,* PHIL *turns and* SOLDIER 1 *hits him. He collapses.*

SOLDIER 2: Come on out, lads!

Shouting savagely, the GREEKS *climb out of the horse and race off. We hear screams, shouts, sirens, bells, etc.* CHLOE *peers out of the horse looking dishevelled. The* SERGEANT *also appears and puts his arm round her.*

CHLOE: Where have they all gone?
SERGEANT: To capture Troy.
CHLOE: Aw. Why haven't you gone with 'em, then?
SERGEANT: 'Cause I'm going to capture you. Come down here.
CHLOE: Oo!

They disappear. Off-stage, the GREEKS *start singing 'We're going to go home', and enter driving the* TROJANS *carrying bags labelled 'Loot'. The* PRIESTESSES *appear hopefully and are seized.* SIMPLEX *wanders on. He is chaired, and* ALL *sing 'For He's a Jolly Good Fellow' and cheer. A placard appears from the horse:* 'MAKE LOVE, NOT WAR'.

[*Curtain.*]

2B OR NOT 2B

CHARACTERS

TEACHER*
POST*
MERLIN

Boys

Knights
KING ARTHUR
LANCELOT
GALAHAD
GAWAIN
TRISTRAM
PERCIVAL
GUY

Squires
KAY
BRYAN
ARNOLD
GARETH
LIONEL
MARK
ECTOR

Girls

Ladies
QUEEN GUINEVERE
ELAINE
ELIZABETH
ETHELREDA
EDITH
MAUD
RHODA

Damsels
BELLE
BLANCHE
ISOBEL
ODETTE
YVONNE
EDWINA
GWYNETH

Doubling: The parts of TEACHER and POST should be doubled. The same player can also take the part of MERLIN.

69

The Play

Two or three tables, a few benches. A hand-bell. A large tablecloth. A
CLASS *are sitting or standing around, mostly talking quietly.*
ARNOLD *appears to hit* GARETH *a fearsome blow in the stomach.*
GARETH *collapses.*

ARNOLD: You ought to yell out.
GARETH: Oh, right. *(He stands.)* Hit me again.

    ARNOLD *appears to hit him again. He gives an enormous yell*
before he falls.

GAWAIN: Shut up, Arnold!
ARNOLD: You shut up.
GARETH *(getting up)*: Hey, you shout this time when you hit me.
ARNOLD: All right. Ready?

    GARETH *nods.* ARNOLD *shouts 'Swine!' and hits him.*
    GARETH *lets out a piercing yell, staggers and collapses, crying.*

BELLE: You've hurt him!

    She crosses to GARETH.

BELLE: Are you all right?

    GARETH *shakes his head.*

ARNOLD: He's only acting. Get up, stupid!
GARETH *(standing, grinning)*: Fooled you! Ha, ha, ha! *(He capers*
    around.) Ha, ha, ha!
ALL: Shut up, Gareth!
GWYNETH *(by the door)*: He's coming!

    ALL *go quiet and stand. Enter* TEACHER.

ALL: Aw!
TEACHER: Are you Form 2B?
ELIZABETH: Or not to be.
TEACHER: What?
ELIZABETH: It's a joke, miss. Mr Chambers always says '2B or
    not 2B'. Are you taking us, miss?

TEACHER: Mr Chambers rang to say he'll not be in today. Has he set you any work?

ALL: No, miss.

ARTHUR: He gives usually gives us an idea, then we improvise.

TEACHER: Such as?

KAY: Last week we did racial discrimination.

BRYAN: We've been prisoners and homeless and out of work.

EDITH: We've done plague, war, famine, family quarrels . . .

BLANCHE: We never do a proper play with costumes and scenery.

ECTOR: Yeah! Let's do Frankenstein!

GIRLS: Aw, no!

ARNOLD: Fighting!

BOYS: Yeah.

ISOBEL: Oh, miss, why do boys always want to fight?

BLANCHE: Miss, let's do a play where we can wear long dresses from the wardrobe!

BELLE: A love story! A romance!

GIRLS: Yes! Please, miss! Please!

BOYS: No!

GIRLS: Yes!

The noise builds up until the TEACHER *blows a whistle.*

TEACHER: That's enough! Listen to me! All of you! The play is going to start. This place is a castle, right?

ALL: Right!

TEACHER: You boys are knights in armour, right?

BOYS: Right!

TEACHER: Girls, you are ladies in long dresses. All right?

GIRLS: All right!

TEACHER: But you all have a problem: you have no money.

Silence.

EDWINA: Miss, I thought knights and ladies were rich.

TEACHER: Not this lot.

KAY: Miss, there's no armour in the wardrobe.

TEACHER: They didn't wear it in the house. Go and get ready.

The CLASS *go out thoughtfully. The* TEACHER *looks round, then spreads a cloth over the tables to make them into one long one. She looks at it, nods, and goes out on the other side. Immediately there is very loud knocking on a door. Enter* GUINEVERE, *still pulling on a long dress. The knocking is repeated. She looks round, realises where the knocking is coming from and opens the door. The* POST *is standing there holding a parcel.*

POST: Good morning. Is this Camelot Castle?

GUINEVERE: Er, yes, that's right.

POST: Is King Arthur in?

GUINEVERE: Yes, he's, er, getting shaved. *(Calling)* Arthur! *(To the* POST*)* He was out late last night with his, er, his knights.

POST: I've got a parcel for him.

GUINEVERE: Oh, I'll take it. I'm his wife.

POST: Then you must be Queen Guinevere?

GUINEVERE: Yes, I must. Yes, I am!

POST: Pleased to meet you. I didn't recognise you without your crown.

GUINEVERE: Well, it just gets in your way round the house. I mean, round the castle.

POST: King Arthur has to sign for this himself, your majesty.

GUINEVERE *(very loud)*: Arthur! Get a move on! It's the post!

Enter ARTHUR *wearing a surcoat with a crown on it and a swordbelt.*

POST: Parcel for you, sire.

ARTHUR: Oh, great! Who's it from?

POST: Er, the Zippo Army Supplies Company.

ARTHUR: It's that new sword I ordered from the catalogue! Give it here.

POST: I'm afraid it's C.O.D., your majesty.

ARTHUR: C.O.D.? That's fish.

GUINEVERE: No! It means Cash On Delivery, Arthur. She wants paying.

ARTHUR: Why don't you pay her, then?

GUINEVERE: 'Cause I haven't had any housekeeping money for the last two months, have I?

ARTHUR: I'll have to give you a cheque.

POST: Sorry, sire. It must be cash, or I'll have to take it back.

ARTHUR: You can't! I broke my other sword last week, killing an evil knight. Look at it!

He draws it. It is broken.

ARTHUR: How can I be a king with a sword like this? And both our crowns are down at the pawnshop!

GUINEVERE: Shut up! *(To the* POST*)* We'll pick it up later. Goodbye.

Exit POST.

GUINEVERE: You didn't have to tell her that, did you?

ARTHUR: Why not? I must be the poorest king in the world, and getting poorer.

GUINEVERE: And whose fault is it?

ARTHUR: Not mine.

GUINEVERE: Well, where does all the money go? It goes on feeding all your knights, Arthur, and their families. You said they were just coming for the weekend. That was seven years ago.

ARTHUR: I am sworn to help all the members of the Round Table!

GUINEVERE: What Round Table? It went for firewood last Christmas to keep 'em all warm. I'm sick of it, Arthur: I can't carry on much longer!

A bell rings.

ARTHUR: Breakfast time. Here they come.

Enter the KNIGHTS, *wearing surcoats and swords, and the* LADIES, *wearing long dresses.*

ALL: Hail, King Arthur!

ARTHUR: And hail to you as well. Pray be seated.

GUINEVERE: I'm afraid we're short of seating: you'll have to squash up.

ALL *just manage to sit.*

GUINEVERE: The food should be here soon.

ALL *look offstage. Silence.*

GUINEVERE: Something's wrong. Ring the bell, Arthur.

ARTHUR *rings the bell.*

ELAINE: Did I see the post bringing a parcel?

ARTHUR: That's right.

ELAINE: Was it something nice?

ARTHUR: A new sword from the catalogue.

LANCELOT: Great! Let's have a look!

ARTHUR: I sent it back.

ELIZABETH: Oh, was it the wrong size?

GUINEVERE: No, we couldn't pay for it.

ARTHUR: Shut up!

GUINEVERE: Why? Let's tell everybody! We are poor, penniless, bankrupt, skint, broke! Now you all know!

Enter KAY, wearing a tabard.

KAY: Did you ring, father?

ARTHUR: Yes, we're waiting for breakfast! Where are the cooks?

KAY: They've all gone.

ALL: Gone!

ETHELREDA: Gone where?

KAY: I don't know. They left a note. Here.

MAUD *(reading)*: 'Dear All, Sorry there is no breakfast, but we are clean out of food. Also we have not been paid for six months. So we are going home. Hope this finds you as it leaves us. Yours truly, Castle Cooks.' And seven kisses.

ARTHUR: They'll get more than kisses when I catch 'em!

RHODA: You're not likely to catch 'em without new horses, are you?

ARTHUR: That's another thing! Whoever heard of seven knights on one horse? No wonder that policeman stopped us.

ELIZABETH: Is there no food at all, Kay?

KAY: We can't find any.

GUINEVERE: Right. Tell Merlin to start your lessons. We'll go down to the shop, girls. And you men had better think hard about ways of making money.

KAY: It's raining.

ELAINE: No matter. Come on!

The LADIES *and* KAY *go out. The* KNIGHTS *spread out.*

ARTHUR *(banging the table)*: I am so frustrated! I'm supposed to be King of England, and I can't even feed my own knights! I've got a broken sword, a crown at the pawnshop and one horse for seven of us. It's the end!

LANCELOT: Cheer up, Arthur. Come on, lads: put your thinking-caps on!

ALL *look thoughtful.*

GALAHAD: What about . . . ? No.

GUY: We could . . . No.

ALL: Why not . . . ? No.

LANCELOT: On your feet! We can't think properly sitting down.

GUY: I don't like thinking: it's not good for me.

LANCELOT: Up, up, up! Stimulate those brain cells!

ALL *wander round, trying to think.*

GAWAIN: What happened to tournaments? We used to go out on a Saturday, do a bit of jousting, a bit of sword-fighting, and you could clear fifty quid on a good afternoon.

TRISTRAM: More if you scored a hat-trick.

PERCIVAL: Nah, nobody goes to tournaments nowadays. Folk

want more violence; rugby, wrestling, American football: that sort of thing.

ALL: Yes.

They resume pacing around.

GUY: I have an idea in my head.

GALAHAD: It must feel lonely. What is it?

GUY: Why don't we find a giant and chop its head off? We used to collect a bounty on giants' heads.

ALL *(disgusted)*: Aw!

GALAHAD: Do you never read the newspapers? *(Picking up a newspaper)* Bloke got fined £1,000 last week for killing a giant.

PERCIVAL: They're a protected species nowadays.

GUY: Yes, you get the League Against Cruel Sports down on you like a ton of bricks.

GAWAIN: What about killing dragons and making 'em into handbags?

TRISTRAM: When did you last see a proper wild dragon?

PERCIVAL: No, it's all toy breeds now: dragon shows at Olympia and chunky morsels to keep their scales shiny.

GALAHAD *(reading paper)*: Hey! This could be it!

PERCIVAL *(looking over GALAHAD'S shoulder)*: What? 'Horse for sale. One careful lady owner. Only 5,000 miles'? You can't trust these dealers: they turn their teeth back.

GALAHAD: Not that! Next to it in the Personal Column. Where it says 'Seven Damsels'.

PERCIVAL: Right! This could be the answer! *(He studies the paper.)*

GUY: What is it, Percival?

PERCIVAL *(to GALAHAD)*: You read it.

GALAHAD *(reading)*: 'Are there seven knights out there who would like to rescue seven attractive damsels from loneliness and boredom? If you're not frightened of risks, the rewards could be high.'

GUY: Rewards! What do you think it's all about?

GAWAIN: It's obvious, isn't it? These seven damsels are rich heiresses who've been captured by an evil knight. *(To GUY)* How do you recognise an evil knight?

GUY: Black armour, black shield, cruel voice, nasty laugh.

GAWAIN: Good man! Now, he's expecting to get a ransom, but these damsels have sneaked out a message to the newspaper, and all we have to do is ride out, rescue 'em, and collect the reward from their rich, grateful parents.

PERCIVAL: Hey!

LANCELOT: What?

PERCIVAL: Why does it need seven knights to rescue the damsels from just one evil knight?

LANCELOT: Perhaps there's seven evil knights.

GUY: Yeah. All with black armour and black shields and black swords.

ALL *(depressed)*: Yes!

LANCELOT: Come on, men! This is our big chance!

TRISTRAM: Wait a minute. How do we know these damsels have rich parents?

LANCELOT: Because this evil knight, or knights, took the trouble to kidnap 'em. Who kidnaps the daughters of the poor? Nobody.

ARTHUR: Good thinking, Lancelot! Let's go!

PERCIVAL: Wait! It's raining. We could get our armour rusty for nothing.

TRISTRAM: And it could be dangerous.

GAWAIN: And expensive. If they're imprisoned in a tall tower we could need to hire scaffolding. That'll cost us.

ALL: Right.

ARTHUR: I can't believe it! Call yourselves knights? Seven damsels in distress are pleading for help! They need us! Who else is going to help 'em?

GUY: Fire Brigade might.

ARTHUR: No! This is a job for knights! This is what we're trained for! There's honour in this!

LANCELOT: And money.

ARTHUR: And money. All agreed? Raise your swords and shout 'Aye!'

ALL *(raising their swords)*: Aye!

TRISTRAM: You need a new sword.

ARTHUR: I know that! Lancelot, leave a note for the wives. Line up, men. Death or glory!

ALL: Death or glory!

ARTHUR: Left turn! By the left, quick march! Left, right! Left, right!

> *They march out.* LANCELOT *finishes the note and runs after them. Enter* MERLIN. *He looks at his watch, shakes his head and rings the bell. Enter the* SQUIRES, *wearing tabards.*

MERLIN: Good morning, squires.

SQUIRES: Good morning, Merlin.

MERLIN: Be seated, young gentlemen. Revision . . .

BRYAN *(raising a hand)*: Merlin, what's the point of us revising?

MERLIN: To make sure that you all know your Knightway Code, and are fit to be knights when your time comes. Repeat your little rhyme.

ALL: We must know our Knightway Code,
    And be good knights on and off the road.

MERLIN: Very good.

BRYAN: But we've no chance of being knights, 'cause our fathers are still alive, and they're all too poor.

ARNOLD: And we've no swords, so we have to practise fighting with our fists, like peasants.

GARETH: And we've no horses to practise riding.

ALL: Right!

KAY: And we ought to be meeting damsels at our age, but we've no money.

ALL: No!

MERLIN: Trust me. My toes were tickling this morning, and that's a good sign. So here's your first question for starters. Kay here mentioned damsels. What is a damsel? Lionel?

LIONEL: Could be a female weasel.

Laughter.

MERLIN: Very witty. Mark?

MARK: Damsel. Oh, yes! A damsel is a fruit, like a plum. Damsel jam.

Laughter.

MERLIN: You're teasing me. Bryan?

BRYAN: A damsel is a maiden, often in distress.

MERLIN: Correct. All repeat it.

ALL: A damsel is a maiden, often in distress.

MERLIN: Good. Now, here's a problem for you. You approach a junction with your lance raised and you meet another knight, also with his lance raised. He dips his lance. What do you do?

ARNOLD: Chop his head off!

BRYAN: No. Run him through!

MERLIN: Well done, Bryan. Run him through. Highway signs now. What's this one?

MARK: Beware ugly giant.

MERLIN: Good. And this?

ECTOR: Beware invisible giant.

MERLIN: Good. And this? It's a tricky one.

KAY: Beware invisible ugly giant.

MERLIN: Well done, Kay. Beware invisible ugly giant.

GARETH: Merlin, if he's invisible, how do you know he's ugly?

MERLIN: Gareth, who's the teacher here?

GARETH: You are.

MERLIN: Correct. Now, more warning signs. First three. Lionel.

LIONEL: Beware wild horses. Beware, er, low-flying dragons.

MERLIN: Good. And . . .?

LIONEL: And, er, dwarfs? Gnomes? Elves?

MERLIN: Anybody?

ALL: Peasants!

LIONEL: Aw, yeah, peasants. I always forget them.

MERLIN: And these three. Mark?

MARK: Beware moat. Beware drawbridge. Beware boiling oil.

MERLIN: Well done! Circular signs now, which mean . . .

ALL: Signs giving orders!

MERLIN: Good! Signs giving orders to . . .

ALL: Peasants!

MERLIN: Very good!

GARETH: Merlin, if the signs are only for peasants, why do we have to learn them?

ALL (*Exasperated*): Oh!

MERLIN: Tell him!

KAY: So we can punish the peasants if they disobey them.

MERLIN: Of course! A few more problems now. A policeman stops a knight and tells him he is obstructing the carriageway. What should the knight do?

ARNOLD: Chop his head off!

LIONEL: Pour boiling oil on him!

ECTOR: No, he should say, 'I go jousting with your Chief Constable.'

MERLIN: Well done, Ector! Now, you remember what a damsel is?

ALL: A damsel is a maiden, often in distress.

MERLIN: Correct. Three ways of rescuing a damsel imprisoned in a tower?

BRYAN: Climb up her hair. Use a rope ladder. Er, fire an arrow with a rope attached.

MERLIN: Splendid! And four ways of killing ogres and giants?

ALL: Lance, sword, mace, boiling oil.

MERLIN: Excellent! And which of these four should you *not* use to kill a dragon?

ECTOR: You should not try killing a dragon with boiling oil for fear of a flash-back fire.

MERLIN: Very good. Now, this has been our last lesson together.

ALL: Aw!

MERLIN: And I've taught you all I know, and all of you are fit to be knights. So just carry on being good squires, and perhaps you'll be made knights sooner than you imagine.

A bell rings.

MERLIN: End of lesson! Off we go to clear the stock-cupboards!

ALL: Aw, Merlin!

MERLIN: Come along, and if you work hard I'll show you a few spells.

They start to go out.

ECTOR: Will you turn Mark into a toad again, Merlin?

MERLIN: I just might.

ECTOR: Oh, great!

They go out. There is a banging on the door, then the LADIES enter, carrying dripping umbrellas and full shopping bags.

GUINEVERE *(slamming her bag down)*: I've never been so humiliated! That shopkeeper says we haven't paid a bill for six months, and I had to beg for credit on this lot. What's Arthur spent all the money on?

ELAINE: Drink, I suppose.

ELIZABETH: It certainly hasn't gone on food.

ETHELREDA: Or clothes.

EDITH: I wonder where they are? *(Calling)* Tristram!

GUINEVERE: Arthur!

MAUD: Here's a note. *(Reading)* 'Dear wives, We have gone to rescue a few damsels. Please clean the castle and air some spare beds. Also make sure there is a lovely meal waiting for us. Yours lovingly, Men.' Men! Huh!

BELLE: Damsels! Remember the last lot they rescued?

ALL: We do!

MAUD: Skirts up to their knees!

EDITH: Painting their toenails!

RHODA: Staying in bed till noon and borrowing all our clothes!

ELAINE: And why should we have to clean up? That's a servant's job.

ETHELREDA: Right. It's not our fault they've all left 'cause they were never paid.

ELAINE: Oh, the last time I had to sweep a spiral staircase I was dizzy for days.

RHODA: And I hate cooking in that kitchen: it's so draughty. And the smells make me sick.

ELAINE: Well, someone has to cook the meals.

ELIZABETH: What about the squires?

Laughter.

EDITH: They'd be worse than the men.

GUINEVERE: And that's another worry.

ETHELREDA: What is?

GUINEVERE: The squires. What sort of example are they getting? They're going to grow up into lazy drunkards like their fathers. And we're going to have to watch it happen.

RHODA: We don't have to watch. I say leave here now. Let them cook their own meals.

MAUD: Talk sense! Where can we go?

ELIZABETH: We can't go back to our parents now.

ELAINE: And who'll give a job to a lady?

EDITH: Anyway, they'd follow us.

ETHELREDA: I know one place where they couldn't follow.

ELAINE: Where's that?

ETHELREDA: A nunnery.

EDITH: What, us: nuns? What sort of life is that?

MAUD: It's not a very exciting life, is it, being a nun?

ETHELREDA: Well, it's not got the sparkle of dusting, or the thrill of washing your husband's clothes in freezing water, if that sort of thing turns you on. But it's regular hours, and I hear they eat well, and you're not woken up every night by your man falling drunk down the stairs.

GUINEVERE: Are you serious?

ETHELREDA: What do you think?

GUINEVERE: Well, what do you others think?

ELAINE: No. I like having men around. I just wish they could earn some money.

EDITH: Yes. And I don't fancy all that praying, do you?

LADIES: No.

ELIZABETH: Right. We'll give them one more chance. Agreed?

ALL: Agreed.

RHODA: Let's go and cook this meal. I'm starving.

> *They start to go.*

MAUD: I hope they don't bring too many damsels, or there won't be enough food to go round.

> *The* LADIES *go out. Offstage, the* KNIGHTS *can be heard laughing and the* DAMSELS *giggling.*

TRISTRAM *(off)*: Ready?

DAMSELS *(off)*: Ready!

TRISTRAM: Close your eyes and in we go!

> *The* KNIGHTS *enter, each leading a* DAMSEL *with her eyes closed.*

ARTHUR: Welcome to:

KNIGHTS: The Great Hall at Camelot!

> *The* DAMSELS *open their eyes, and look round, clearly disappointed.*

GWYNETH: It's not very big, is it?

PERCIVAL: It's a lot bigger than that tower we rescued you from.

ODETTE: You're right: it's a lovely room. It's so, er, cool.

YVONNE: And, er, simple.

LANCELOT: Yes, nothing fancy round here.

ISOBEL: Have you no more furniture?

GALAHAD: Had to burn it.

EDWINA: What?

ARTHUR: Burnet. Mr Burnet, the wood chap, he's taken most of it away to, er, polish it.

BELLE: Oh. You know, what this room needs is a woman's touch. It's easy to see that you men aren't married.

Enter EDITH.

EDITH: Who are all these girls?

TRISTRAM: They're the seven damsels we've just rescued.

EDITH: And I suppose they're expecting a meal?

DAMSELS: Yes, please!

EDITH: Well, one of you will have to go to the shop.

TRISTRAM: They can't go. I'll send the boy. *(Calling)* Lionel!

Enter LIONEL. *The* DAMSELS *stare at him.*

LIONEL *(staring at the* DAMSELS*)*: Yes?

EDITH: Stop staring. You have to go down to the shop.

LIONEL: Can I take the horse?

ARTHUR: You scratched it last time you borrowed it.

LIONEL: I'll be careful, honest. What do I want?

EDITH: Seven syllabubs, seven portions of wild boar.

LIONEL: Aw, why are we having wild boar again?

EDITH: Because it's on offer! Tell him to book it. And go out the back way.

Exit LIONEL.

EDITH: And don't blame us if it's late!

Exit EDITH.

ISOBEL: Who is that coarse woman?

TRISTRAM: Oh, it's just, er, one of the cooks.

ODETTE: And who's the young man?

TRISTRAM: He's a squire. We've seven squires.

DAMSELS: Oh!

ISOBEL: I wonder if you men could leave us alone for a little while? We're only weak women, and we need a rest.

ARTHUR: By Jove, I was forgetting! Come on, chaps, let's go and chase up the meal!

GAWAIN: Last man into the kitchen's a woman!

The KNIGHTS *run out, shouting.*

YVONNE: What a dump! Look at it!

BLANCHE: No carpets, no tapestries, no ornaments, no proper furniture!

YVONNE: I blame you!

BLANCHE: Me? Why me?

YVONNE *(pushing her)*: You know why!

ODETTE: Leave her!

YVONNE: It was her idea to put that advert in the paper! Her and her stupid romantic novels!

BLANCHE: They are not stupid! *(To* BELLE*)* Are they?

BELLE: No, they're out of this world. I've got one here. Listen! *(Reading)* 'He was a knight in shining armour. She was a beautiful damsel. He set her on his milk-white charger and swept her away to his fabulous castle, adorned with costly tapestries and sparkling with rich jewels.'

YVONNE: I haven't seen much shining armour round here, have you? And where are all these tapestries and jewels?

ISOBEL: They did bring a white horse to rescue us, didn't they?

GWYNETH: Oh yes, they did. Pulling a cart with a damn great sign saying 'United Dairies'.

EDWINA: When we stopped at the lights and that woman asked me for three pints of gold-top and six yogurts I could have brained her.

BLANCHE: No, it's not like that in the books. But you all voted to get out of the tower, didn't you?

DAMSELS *(gloomily)*: Yes.

ISOBEL: And at least there's more room here.

DAMSELS *(gloomily)*: Yes.

ODETTE: I could stand the castle. I just can't stand those men.

DAMSELS: Right!

ISOBEL: In your romances, what do the heroes talk about?

BLANCHE: Oh, they tell the heroine how beautiful she is: how her lips are like cherries and her hair is like a field of corn rippling in the wind.

BELLE: And how he'll love her for all eternity.

BLANCHE: Yes, and how he'll do anything to make her happy.

ODETTE: You're sure that's what heroes talk about?

BELLE
BLANCHE } Oh yes, always.

ODETTE: In that case, we've got the wrong heroes. What do this lot talk about?

GWYNETH: Which pubs sell real ale.

EDWINA: How to cure a hangover.

YVONNE: How to use bat–dung to get mould off your shield.

ISOBEL: The best way to chop a man's head off.

ALL: Eucch!

ODETTE *(to BLANCHE)*: What about yours?

BLANCHE: Do you really want to know?

ALL: Yes.

BLANCHE: All right: six ways of disembowelling a dragon.

ALL: Eucch!

ODETTE *(to BELLE)*: What did yours talk about?

BELLE: He kept saying, 'I bet the ransom will be a pretty penny.'

GWYNETH: What's that mean?

BELLE: Search me. I think he was drunk.

YVONNE: Weren't they all?

ALL: Yes.

GWYNETH: And another thing: I'm sure they're all married.

ISOBEL: So what do we do? I'm not staying here with them.

ODETTE: No way.

YVONNE: But we can't go back and say, 'Please can we have our room in the tower again?' Specially after that goodbye note we left him.

Laughter.

GWYNETH: What say we sneak out now?

EDWINA: Where to?

GWYNETH: I don't know: I don't care! Come on!

They look at each other.

ODETTE: Well, there's nothing to keep us here. Agreed?

ALL: Agreed!

GYNETH: Right, let's move.

They start to move.

MERLIN *(off)*: Through there!

Enter the SQUIRES *carrying boxes, clothes, etc. They cross the room and go out. The* DAMSELS *roll their eyes and stare after them.*

MERLIN: Sorry to disturb you, ladies!
GWYNETH *(staring after the* SQUIRES*)*: That's all right.

Exit MERLIN.

DAMSELS *(ecstatic)*: Ooh!
YVONNE: What were we talking about?
ODETTE: Erm, I was saying that there's nothing to keep us here.

Enter MERLIN.

MERLIN: Good morning! My name is Merlin. I'm the court magician and tutor. And you must be the damsels who've been rescued. Is there anything I can do to help you?
EDWINA: You could tell us who those young men are.
MERLIN: Oh, those are my pupils, the squires. They've just finished their course and are fit to be knighted. Do you think they look fit?
DAMSELS: Very fit.
BLANCHE: And are any of them betrothed to be married?
MERLIN: I'm afraid not. They hardly ever leave the castle, and they never go to parties.
BLANCHE: Perhaps we could help them?
DAMSELS: Mm!
MERLIN: I wish you could. I must go.

Exit MERLIN. *Enter* KNIGHTS.

ARTHUR: We must talk to you!
ISOBEL: Do you have to? I'm famished.
ARTHUR: You'll have to wait: the gas pressure's low.

DAMSELS *(disappointed)*: Aw!

LANCELOT: Let's not waste time. We must write letters to your parents.

DAMSELS: Our parents? Which parents?

GAWAIN: Don't be stupid! We've rescued you, right?

DAMSELS: Right.

ISOBEL: Well, in a way.

GAWAIN: So now we tell your loving parents that you're free.

GALAHAD: Free at a price.

ISOBEL: What do you mean?

GALAHAD: You're free to go once your rich daddies have paid us the reward that you offered in the paper.

ARTHUR: And we shall have money to buy food and armour and swords and . . .

TRISTRAM: Beer.

GAWAIN: Beer. Right?

DAMSELS: Wrong.

KNIGHTS: Wrong?

DAMSELS: Right.

GUY: I can't follow this.

BELLE: You've made a mistake about the reward.

ARTHUR: We have not! *(To GALAHAD)* Read the advert they put in the paper!

GALAHAD *(reading)*: 'Are there seven knights who would like to rescue seven damsels from loneliness and boredom? The rewards . . .'

GAWAIN: Rewards! We want the rewards!

KNIGHTS: Right!

ODETTE: Sit down!

KNIGHTS: Why should we . . .

DAMSELS *(pointing)*: Sit!

The KNIGHTS *sit, bemused.*

ODETTE: You've all made a mistake.

GAWAIN: How?

ODETTE: Well, for a start we hadn't been kidnapped.

PERCIVAL: I thought that was an easy rescue. Just opening the door.

EDWINA: We were lodging with our guardian, and he was very strict, wasn't he?

BELLE: In at ten.

BLANCHE: No make-up.

ODETTE: No new clothes.

YVONNE: No parties.

ISOBEL: No fun.

EDWINA: So we put that advert in the paper for a laugh.

LANCELOT: But what's the reward?

YVONNE: It's not cash.

LANCELOT: You mean, it's like treasure?

BLANCHE: More like leisure. We decided to reward our rescuers by letting them take us out.

PERCIVAL: Take you out? Where?

BLANCHE: To romantic nightspots!

ISOBEL: Super little restaurants!

BELLE: Parties!

GWYNETH: Tournaments!

EDWINA: Jousting!

YVONNE: Feasting!

ODETTE: Spending money like water!

DAMSELS: Having fun!

TRISTRAM: Fun! We thought your rich parents would pay us. You see . . . we've no money.

DAMSELS: No money!

KNIGHTS: No.

DAMSELS: Oh.

ISOBEL: And we've no parents.

KNIGHTS: No parents!

DAMSELS: Not one!

ARTHUR: I don't believe it!

LANCELOT: I won't believe it!

GUY: They're lying!

GALAHAD: You don't expect us to believe that not one of you has a parent living?

DAMSELS: Not one.

GALAHAD: Seven fathers, seven mothers: all dead?

DAMSELS: One father, one mother.

KNIGHTS: You don't mean . . . ?

DAMSELS: Yes! We are sisters!

KNIGHTS: Sisters!

BELLE: And orphans.

KNIGHTS: Orphans!

BLANCHE: Stop repeating everything, or we'll never get to the end of the play.

KNIGHTS: Sorry.

BLANCHE: That's all right. We're all the daughters of Sir Bertram de Bors and the Lady Melisande.

EDWINA: The late Sir Bertram.

GWYNETH: And the late Lady Melisande.

ARTHUR: And it's a bit late to tell us all this now. How did they die?

ODETTE: They were killed when their coach overturned. Going too fast.

GUY: Coach Express, was it?

ODETTE: Their private coach. Returning from a late-night tournament.

GALAHAD: But what happened to all their wealth?

YVONNE: They left all their money . . .

KNIGHTS: Yes?

EDWINA: And all their castles . . .

KNIGHTS: Yes, yes?

GWYNETH: To our brothers.

KNIGHTS: Aw!

ODETTE: So we have no money. We thought you were rich knights.

ARTHUR: And we thought you were rich damsels.

ODETTE: I'm sorry.

LANCELOT: Not as sorry as we are.

GALAHAD: Wait till our wives hear about it.
KNIGHTS: Oh, no!
GAWAIN *(standing)*: We've rescued 'em for nothing!
TRISTRAM: *(standing)*: We've been conned!
PERCIVAL *(standing)*: Chuck 'em out!
GUY: *(standing)*: They're cheats! Chop their heads off!
KNIGHTS: Yeah!

    The DAMSELS *scream in fright.*

ARTHUR: Stop! We can't kill visitors in our own house! There'll be blood all over the floor! Take 'em outside!
DAMSELS *(kneeling)*: Help!

    There is a roll of thunder. MERLIN *appears wearing a splendid costume.*

KNIGHTS: Merlin!
DAMSELS *(standing)*: Merlin!
ARTHUR: What are you doing here? You're supposed to be giving the squires their lessons.
MERLIN: It's you who need teaching a lesson!

    Enter GUINEVERE.

GUINEVERE: What's all the screaming?
MERLIN: Come in, ladies!

    Enter the LADIES.

GUY: They're supposed to be cooking!
MERLIN: You knights are very good at telling others what to do, aren't you?

    He claps. Enter the SQUIRES.

DAMSELS *(smitten by* SQUIRES*)*: Oh!
SQUIRES *(smitten by* DAMSELS*)*: Ah!
GUY: And these squires should . . .
MERLIN: Well?
GUY: They should . . .

MERLIN: They should listen to a strange tale! Hearken! These
   damsels are the orphan daughters of Sir Bertram de Bors . . .
LADIES: Ooh!
OTHERS: Shh!
MERLIN: Who left all his money and castles to his sons.
GUINEVERE: Typical!
LADIES: Right!
MERLIN: But!
ALL *(except* DAMSELS*)*: But!
MERLIN: To his daughters he gave . . .
ALL *(except* DAMSELS*)*: Yes, yes?
DAMSELS *(producing them)*: Necklaces!
OTHERS: Necklaces!
MERLIN: Seven gold necklaces.
KNIGHTS: Seven gold necklaces.
ARTHUR: Gold! That's more like it!

He grabs the nearest necklace and examines it.

ARTHUR: This isn't gold! It's only brass!
GUY: Chop off their . . . awk!

He freezes, silent, as MERLIN *points at him.*

MERLIN: If you shout once more, I shall turn you into a toad.

He snaps his fingers, and GUY *relaxes.*

LANCELOT: You said these necklaces were gold.
MERLIN: So they were. Sir Bertram summoned the finest
   goldsmith in the land, who made seven necklaces set with
   precious stones and made of pure gold . . .
LANCELOT: But they're made of . . . ah!

   MERLIN *freezes him as before.*

MERLIN: Pure gold. But when they were finished, Sir Bertram
   began to fear that the necklaces would be stolen and his
   daughters left penniless. So he summoned a magician called –

   He snaps his fingers and points at LANCELOT.

LANCELOT: Merlin.

MERLIN: Merlin, who laid a spell on them, which turned the gold into brass and the rich jewels into glass. But!

ALL: But!

MERLIN: But the spell will be reversed if the damsels marry seven poor knights!

KNIGHTS (*stepping forward*): Seven poor knights!

LADIES: You're married!

KNIGHTS: Divorce us!

LADIES: Never!

KNIGHTS: Oh, shucks!

They step back.

KAY: Would seven poor squires do?

SQUIRES (*nodding eagerly*): Seven poor squires?

DAMSELS (*eagerly*): Seven poor squires?

MERLIN: No. It must be seven poor knights.

ALL: Oh.

ODETTE: Well, there's nothing more to say. Thank you for rescuing us. I'm sorry we can't help you. We'll leave now. Goodbye.

The DAMSELS start shaking hands and saying 'Goodbye' to the OTHERS.

YVONNE: Goodbye, Merlin.

MERLIN: Why must you go?

YVONNE: You know why: because we can't marry the squires.

EDWINA: If we did, we'd be penniless. Goodbye.

MERLIN: Wait! King Arthur! Step forward and show us your sword.

ARTHUR starts to draw his sword, then hesitates.

MERLIN: What's wrong?

ARTHUR: It's broken. I'm a king without a sword.

MERLIN points at the sheath. There is a magical sound.

MERLIN: Broken is mended,
Started is ended.
Ended is trouble,
Knights shall double.

ARTHUR *slowly draws his sword; it is whole.* ALL *exclaim.*

MERLIN: Now, my pupils, what is the noblest use of a knightly sword?

ARNOLD *(raising a hand)*: Is it chopping people's heads off?

MERLIN: It is not! What is the *noblest* use?

BRYAN *(raising a hand)*: The noblest use of a knightly sword is dubbing.

MERLIN: Correct. And what is dubbing?

SQUIRES: Making someone into a knight.

BRYAN: Dubbing is to confer knighthood by striking the shoulder with the flat of the blade.

MERLIN: Correct again. And we all see a blade ready for use.

GUY: You don't mean making these youngsters into knights at their age?

RHODA: You were younger when you were dubbed.

GUY: Well.

GUINEVERE: What do you damsels say? It's your choice.

MERLIN: Well, shall they be dubbed knights?

DAMSELS: Yes, please!

MERLIN: When?

DAMSELS: Now!

MERLIN: And do their parents give consent?

KNIGHTS ⎫
LADIES ⎭ : We do

MERLIN: And finally, does the king give his consent?

ARTHUR: Er . . .

GUINEVERE: He does.

ARTHUR: I do.

Laughter.

ARTHUR: Silence! Squires line up there, and damsels opposite.

Squires kneel. Right knee. Do you all swear to defend the right, ever tempering justice with mercy? Answer, 'We do.'
SQUIRES: We do.

ARTHUR *dubs them by tapping them on the shoulder and saying, 'Arise, Sir Kay,' etc.*

ARTHUR: I proclaim you all knights!

Applause.

ARTHUR: Merlin, would you take over?
MERLIN: Most willingly. Step forward, damsels. Take the hand of your chosen knight.

Music.

MERLIN: Do you seven knights take these damsels to be your lawful wedded wives? Answer, 'We do.'
SQUIRES: We do.
MERLIN: And do you damsels take these knights to be your lawful wedded husbands? Answer . . .
DAMSELS: We do!
MERLIN: I pronounce you all man and wife, er, men and wives. Well, married!

Applause.

MERLIN: And now Merlin bids you all farewell!

Magic sound. He starts to spin.

DAMSELS: Merlin!
ALL: Merlin!

MERLIN *and the music stop.*

MERLIN: Yes?
DAMSELS: Our necklaces are still brass!
MERLIN: Silly me! I need a cloth. *(Seeing the table cloth)* This will do nicely. *(He lifts it.)* All place your necklaces together on the table! *(He covers them with the cloth.)* All close your eyes! No

peeping! *(Passing his hands over the cloth)*
> Abracadabra! Spirits timid, spirits bold,
> Turn this brassware into gold!

Magic sound.

> Abracadabra! Spirits kindly, spirits cruel,
> Turn each stone into a jewel!

Magic sound. MERLIN *lifts the cloth to reveal gold necklaces.* ALL *exclaim.*

MERLIN: Gold for the brides!

The DAMSELS *put on the necklaces. Applause.*

MERLIN: Another little spell! Abracadabra!
> Pockets and purses you shall find
> With golden coins all newly lined!

Magic noise. ALL *produce gold coins and exclaim.*

MERLIN: And now, Merlin bids you all . . .

He prepares to spin.

GUINEVERE: Merlin! I forbid you to go: you must stay to the wedding feast. Arthur can pop down to the shop for the cake.

Laughter.

GUINEVERE: And we'd all like to thank you for helping us and bringing our play to a happy ending.

ALL applaud MERLIN. *A bell rings.*

MERLIN: I must go: I have another lesson to teach. But perhaps someone *(gesturing to the audience)* would like to applaud all of you.

ALL line up for a curtain call and MERLIN *starts the applause.*

[*Curtain.*]

TAP TAP

CHARACTERS

HARRY PORTER, *a newspaper man*
JACKIE, *a youth hostel warden*

Teachers	**Hitch-hikers**
MISS (GWYNETH)	LIZ
SIR (RAYMOND)	TRISH

Oldies

FRANK	JESSIE
HERBERT	MAGGIE
PERCY	WINNIE
CHARLIE	POLLY

Kids

ANDREW	ANN
CARLTON	BETH
JOHN	CLARE
PAUL	EMMA
SIMON	PENNY
TIM	RACHEL
WILLIAM	SARAH

The events of the play take place in the common-room of a small old youth hostel high on the moors, on an October evening and the next morning.

The Play

*The common-room of a small, old-fashioned youth hostel, formerly a pub.
There are two doors: one to the outside, the other to the rest of the
building. Near the inner door is what used to be a bar. On it, a bell and
a phone. A cupboard with games and books, and a noticeboard. Upstage:
tables with benches on them. Downstage near the inner door: chairs round
a fire.*

As the curtain rises PORTER, *wearing outdoor clothes, is kneeling
and replacing a loose panel on the bar. He taps it into place as* JACKIE
enters and starts to take down a picture. PORTER *hurts himself.*

PORTER: Aaaargh!

JACKIE *(startled)*: What are you doing?

PORTER *(nursing his thumb)*: Shush! Don't alarm the warden!

JACKIE: I am the warden, and I am alarmed. Are you one of the
    workmen?

PORTER: Er, yes. I'm checking a . . . gas-pipe.

JACKIE: We don't have gas.

PORTER: Electric, then.

JACKIE: You're not a workman at all, are you?

PORTER: No, I'm on a job . . . Er, a job scheme. Just for the day.

JACKIE: Oh, I see. I know all the other workmen. They've built
    new washrooms and a new kitchen. Trouble is, they've pulled
    down the old dormitories and now the money's run out. What
    use is a youth hostel with only ten beds?

She sits, dejected.

PORTER: Do you usually get a lot of visitors?

JACKIE: I wish we did. A few walkers and cyclists. We're a long
    way from the main road, so we never see a hitch-hiker, thank
    God. Anyway, unless we can find more money this place closes
    down tomorrow, after 300 years. It used to be a pub called the
    Red Lion.

A whistle blows.

JACKIE: That's your knocking-off whistle.

PORTER: Is it? I'll leave you, then. I hope you find the money.

JACKIE: You don't find it just lying around, do you?

PORTER: Not unless you're smart. *(In the doorway)* Did you see this morning's paper?

JACKIE: No papers round here.

PORTER: Pity. Do you know what this place was called before it was the Red Lion?

JACKIE: No, I've forgotten. Does it matter?

PORTER: It could. 'Bye!

> *Exit* PORTER.

JACKIE: Funny fellow!

> *Exit* JACKIE *with the picture. There is a knock on the outer door, then* JOHN *bursts in, followed by* TIM, *who stays near the door.* JOHN *puts down his rucksack and sits. Both wear walking gear.*

TIM: She said stand outside, didn't she?

JOHN: Huh! Nobody makes me stand outside, mate, not after tramping fifteen flipping miles. It's like a swamp out there. Let the others stand in it.

TIM: They are doing.

JOHN: More fool them.

TIM *(looking round)*: I bet there's ghosts here: noises in the night.

JOHN: There's noises in my stomach: I'm starving. Have a crisp.

TIM *(crossing)*: Oh, thanks.

> *He sits. Enter* MISS.

MISS: Out!

> *They leap to their feet.*

JOHN: Please, miss . . .

MISS: Out! What did Sir say?

JOHN: Please, miss . . .

MISS: What were you told?

TIM: Wait outside till the teachers come.

MISS: Right! Out, sharpish!

> *They start to go out.*

Tap Tap

MISS: Take your rucksacks!

They all go out. Enter JACKIE *carrying a dishcloth.*

JACKIE: Hello! Must be hearing things now. I'm going barmy.

Exit JACKIE.

MISS *(off)*: Right! In you go!

Enter MISS *and the* KIDS.

MISS: Where's Sir?
JOHN: He's coming, miss.

JACKIE *backs into the room carrying a chair and singing to herself.*

MISS: Good evening!
JACKIE: Great jumping Scott! Don't tell me you're all on a job scheme?
MISS: We're your party.
JACKIE *(putting the chair by the fire)*: Come again? Whose party?
MISS: Your school party. The sponsored walk party. You can't have forgotten us?
JACKIE *(bitterly)*: Oh no: I couldn't forget you.
MISS: We booked months ago, just for tonight.
JACKIE: Oh no. No, you didn't.
MISS: Oh yes. Yes, we did. Fetch the warden.
JACKIE: I am the warden.

Enter SIR.

SIR: Hello again, everybody!
KIDS: Hello, sir!
MISS: Raymond! The warden here claims we haven't booked.
SIR: Nonsense, of course we've booked! *(To* JACKIE*)* Here's your letter. *(Reading)* 'Dear Sir, I have booked your party as follows: 1 adult male, 1 adult female, 7 young males, 7 young females, 16 evening meals, 16 breakfasts, for the night of the thirteenth of the ninth.'
MISS: The ninth!

JACKIE *nods grimly.*

SIR: Today. The thirteenth of October.
MISS: Children: tell Sir which is the ninth month.

> The KIDS *recite the months, counting on their fingers and finishing on 'September' very loud.* BETH *starts to cry.*

MISS: Raymond, you booked us all in for *last* month.
SIR: Oh dear! Silly old me!
KIDS: Aw, sir!
JACKIE *(snatching the letter)*: A month ago I bought two large
   bottles of tomato sauce, I peeled and chipped a mound of
   potatoes, I heated two large pans of baked beans, I made sixteen
   large helpings of blackberry crumble, and I put clean cloths and
   flowers on all the tables, and *you never came!*
KIDS: Aw, sir!

> BETH *sobs.*

JACKIE: And I waited and waited while all the food went cold.
   (She sits.) Then I cried.
KIDS: Aw!
SIR: I don't suppose it's still around?
JACKIE *(leaping up)*: If it was still around, it'd be walking! I threw
   it to the hens!
SIR: Lucky hens, eh? Sorry about that! Well, we're only a month
   late! I suppose we can have a bed for the night?
JACKIE: A bed? You all going to sleep in one bed?
SIR: What?
JACKIE: You ever notice anything, like all that scaffolding
   outside? Do you ever read anything?

> *She takes down a notice and thrusts it at* ANN.

JACKIE: Read that!
ANN *(reading)*: 'On September 15th the party annexe at the
   Moorland Hostel will close for extensive rebuilding, and
   accommodation will be strictly limited.'

JACKIE: And now the money's run out. Tomorrow we close.
MISS: Oh. And how many beds are there for tonight?
JACKIE: Ten.
MISS *(looking at* KIDS*)*: Ten.
JACKIE: And eight of them are booked.
MISS: Oh no! What time is it?
SIR: Nearly six.
MISS: And how far away is the next hostel?
JACKIE: Twenty-three miles.
MISS: Is that a hotel down the lane?
JACKIE: No: just a pub.
MISS: Nearest town?
JACKIE: Seven miles.
MISS: Buses? Trains?
JACKIE: You're joking.
KIDS: Aw!

> KIDS *and* TEACHERS *sit glumly. We hear whistling. Enter* LIZ *and* TRISH*, not in walking clothes, carrying cases.* TRISH *chews constantly.*

JACKIE: Good evening.
LIZ: You the whatsit? The landlady?
JACKIE: The warden.
LIZ: Sounds like a prison, dunnit? Any spare beds?
JACKIE: Two.
LIZ: We'll have 'em. Right, Trish?
TRISH: Yeah.
JACKIE: I'll book you in later. Are you self-cookers?
LIZ: How do you mean, self-cookers?
JACKIE: Are you going to cook yourselves?
LIZ: No, we wouldn't fit in the pan.

> TRISH *gives a loud laugh, followed by the* KIDS.

JACKIE: Very witty. I'll show you where you sleep.

> *They start to go out.*

JACKIE: Have you walked far?

TRISH ⎫
LIZ ⎭ : Nah.

> JACKIE, LIZ *and* TRISH *go out.*

ANDREW: What are we going to do, sir?

SIR: Walk to the town.

KIDS: Aw no, sir!

PENNY: I just can't walk seven miles!

SARAH: I just can't walk one mile.

RACHEL: I just can't walk!

> *Laughter.*

RACHEL: I've got blisters like gooseberries, miss!

WILLIAM: My legs are like jelly.

TIM: What flavour?

WILLIAM: Plum flavour.

TIM: Why plum?

WILLIAM: 'Cause I'm plumb wore-out, pardner.

> KIDS *groan.*

SIR: We'll have to walk: there's no option.

PAUL: If we have to walk any further we'll die.

KIDS: Yeah!

ANN: And you'll both go to prison.

SIR: You'd like that, wouldn't you?

KIDS: Yeah!

WILLIAM: Worth dying for.

> *Laughter.*

BETH: It's all right laughing, but it's starting to rain and it's cold and I'm tired out!

> BETH *bursts into tears as her friends shush and comfort her. Enter* JACKIE.

JACKIE: What's wrong now?

MISS: What's wrong? We're stuck in the middle of nowhere, that's what's wrong!

EMMA: We'll never buy a minibus now.

MISS *(to* JACKIE*)*: We're on a sponsored week's walk to raise £10,000 for a school minibus. This is our first day.

JACKIE: And your last, by the look of it. I suppose you booked all the other hostels for the ninth month?

SIR: Well, er, yes, I did.

KIDS: Aw, sir!

JACKIE: And you haven't a chance of getting in anywhere now.

MISS: And you've no spare beds?

JACKIE: We've no space. Two small bedrooms, washrooms, kitchen and this room. That's the lot.

CLARE: Why can't we sleep in here?

KIDS: Yes!

JACKIE: Because it's a common-room. Youth hostel rules.

MISS: Who's in the other eight beds?

JACKIE: The Autumn Leaves.

KIDS: Autumn Leaves?

JACKIE: Yes, it's a cycling club for old people.

CLARE Old people! I thought this was a youth hostel, not an old folks' home.

JACKIE: Any one of any age can stay at a youth hostel. Didn't you know? Anyway they're young at heart, so they are youth in a way.

ANDREW: So why can't this be a dormitory in a way?

EMMA: Let's stay. Please!

KIDS: Please! Please! Please!

Pause. ALL *stare at* JACKIE.

JACKIE: Oh, all right.

The KIDS *cheer and dance with delight. Enter the* OLDIES: FRANK, HERBERT, PERCY, CHARLIE, JESSIE, MAGGIE, WINNIE *and* POLLY. *They are grey-haired and bespectacled, wearing caps and baggy shorts and carrying cycle-bags. They stand inside the doorway shaking the rain off their anoraks or taking off their capes while they exclaim merrily. Gradually both groups become aware of each other and fall silent, staring. The KIDS smile at first, while the OLDIES scowl.*

MAGGIE: Youngsters!

OLDIES: Kids!

FRANK: A party!

OLDIES: School party!

JACKIE: Good evening! You've booked, I believe?

HERBERT: We certainly have! *(Giving her cards)* Eight senior cyclists.

JACKIE: That's right.

JESSIE: No, it is not right, young woman! You told me on the telephone that it would be quiet here tonight: no parties, no kids. And look at 'em: it's like the Pied Piper was here!

JACKIE: I'm afraid there's been a mistake in the booking, but I'm sure there will be no problem.

HERBERT: Well, my problem is I'm starving. Let's get in the kitchen before these kids take over.

The OLDIES agree, pick up their kit and cross to the door.

HERBERT: What's the meal?

MAGGIE: Oxtail soup.

FRANK: Steak and kidney pie.

WINNIE: Jacket potatoes.

PERCY: Cauliflower.

JESSIE: Creamed carrots.

CHARLIE: Gooseberry fool.

POLLY: Double cream.

FRANK: Cheese and biscuits.

They go out.

KIDS *(yearning)*: Ooh!

PENNY: What are we having to eat?

PAUL: Yeah, I'm famished.

The KIDS *agree and look at the* TEACHERS.

MISS: Well, we haven't brought any food with us, so we'll hear what the warden has in her store.

ALL *look at* JACKIE, *who is doing some paper work.*

JACKIE: Sorry?
SIR *(smiling)*: Food.
CARLTON: In your store.
PENNY: Any fish and chips?
PAUL: Pies and peas?
EMMA: Hamburgers?
JOHN: Fish fingers?

JACKIE *shakes her head at all these, and the* KIDS' *faces fall.*

SARAH: Have you got anything for an evening meal?

JACKIE *nods.*

SARAH: What?
JACKIE: Soup.
ALL: *Soup?*
JACKIE: Celery soup.
ALL: Celery soup? Is that all?
JACKIE: Just about. We close tomorrow.
SIR: Soup it is then! Yummy, eh?
KIDS *(glum)*: Yummy scrummy.
PENNY: Soup doesn't fill you up: it just sloshes about inside you. I need something solid.
SIR *(advancing on her)*: How about a tap on the . . .
MISS: Raymond! Stop it!
JACKIE: Come through and I'll give you the soup.

JACKIE *and* TEACHERS *go out. The* KIDS *sit dejected.*

TIM: Celery soup! Huh!
SARAH: And what are we going to do tomorrow?
SIMON: No use walking to the next hostel, 'cause it'll be full.

BETH: I want to go home.

ANDREW: What about the minibus?

BETH: Don't care. I'm going to eat myself sick when I get home.

Enter TRISH and LIZ, eating. They stare at the KIDS, then LIZ whispers to TRISH, who nods. They sit by the fire, while the KIDS stare.

LIZ: You lot walk here?

KIDS: Yeah.

ANN: Right across the moors. With blisters.

LIZ: Your teachers must be stupid, making you walk.

TRISH: We itch.

ANN: Pardon?

LIZ: We itch.

PAUL: Well, scratch.

LIZ: Nah! We '*itch*. All over.

CLARE: You probably need a shower.

LIZ: Nah! You don't get us. We 'itch all over.

TRISH: England, Scotland, Wales. All over.

LIZ: We're '*itch-'ikers*!

CLARE: Oh, *hitch-hikers*!

LIZ: That's what we said.

TRISH: We done 150 miles today.

BOYS: Wow!

CARLTON: Why did you come so far?

LIZ: Something we read in the paper.

CARLTON: What about?

TRISH (*grinning slyly*): Taps.

KIDS: Taps?

Enter MISS.

MISS: The meal's just about ready. Come through and wash your hands.

The KIDS start to go out.

CLARE: What are we doing tomorrow, miss?

MISS: We'll, er, decide in the morning. Come along.

MISS and the KIDS go out. TRISH and LIZ instantly stand and start searching the room, tapping round the edges.

LIZ: Where's the old bloke's paper?
TRISH: I hid it in the kitchen.
LIZ: Stupid old bat.
TRISH *(staring by the fire)*: Come here!
LIZ: What?
TRISH: There might have been a tap here, for a boiler.
LIZ *(examining the area)*: Nothing.

Enter the OLD MEN.

HERBERT: That was a first-rate meal.
FRANK: Grand!
CHARLIE: Have you two lost something?
TRISH: Nah.
PERCY: I've lost my newspaper. Have you seen it?
TRISH: Nah.
LIZ: Come on, kid.

LIZ and TRISH go out.

FRANK: A funny pair.
CHARLIE: At any rate, they're not noisy. Come and sit by the fire and make room for the womenfolk.

The OLD MEN spread out the chairs, throwing the KIDS' clothes onto the tables, then they sit and read. Enter the OLD WOMEN.

CHARLIE: Here you are, ladies! Come and rest your legs!
POLLY: Ee, this is nice!

ALL sit. The LADIES read or knit.

WINNIE: Lovely.

One after another, the OLDIES yawn and sleep. Enter the KIDS, chattering. They shush each other and fall silent, staring in dismay at the sleeping OLDIES and the rearranged furniture.

JOHN: Look at that. It's not fair!

ANDREW: They're taking up half the room!

WILLIAM: Tell 'em to move!

TIM: Yes! Tell the warden they're sleeping in the common-room and it's against the rules.

BOYS: Yeah!

GIRLS: Shhh!

CLARE: We've got to be quiet, or she'll get mad.

> FRANK *snores: the* KIDS *giggle.*

ANN: There's some books here. And games: cards, dominoes, Scrabble.

> *The* KIDS *crowd round the games, beginning to chatter.* FRANK *snores very loud. They giggle, then shush each other and settle down as best they can round the tables. Enter the* TEACHERS *in outdoor clothing.*

TIM: Where are you going, sir?

SIR: Miss and I are going for a walk.

BOYS: Wor!

MISS: Shush! All be good while we're out!

JOHN: And you!

> *The* KIDS *giggle.*

MISS: We'll be back before bedtime.

SIMON: Can I come with you, miss?

SIR: No, Simon. Just play quietly.

MISS: Goodbye, children.

KIDS: Goodbye, miss!

> *The* TEACHERS *go out.*

EMMA: They're going to the pub.

WILLIAM: Yeah. Drinking all night.

PENNY: And eating. They serve food.

KIDS: Cor!

BETH: I'm starving!

TIM: Come on. Let's play a game like they said.
ANN: I spy with my little eye something beginning with R.
CLARE: Room? Rachel? Rubbish hostel?
ANN: Do you give up? Rinklies!

> ANN *gestures at the* OLDIES *and pulls an old face. They snort with laughter.* FRANK *snores and opens his eyes. The* KIDS *freeze.* FRANK *closes his eyes. The* KIDS *carry on playing.* ANDREW, PAUL SIMON *and* WILLIAM *are playing "Cheat" in a game that gets gradually louder.*

ANDREW: Two clubs.
OTHERS: Cheat!
PAUL: Three diamonds.
OTHERS: Cheat!
SIMON: Four Kings!
OTHERS: Cheat!!
WILLIAM: Five aces!
OTHERS: Cheat!!

> HERBERT *snores very loudly and wakes. The* KIDS *laugh.*

HERBERT (*standing*): I've had enough of this! We came here for peace and quiet, not to hear you youngsters shouting and bawling at each other all night!
OLDIES: (*waking up*): That's right!
FRANK: You think you can do as you like!
OLDIES: That's right!
FRANK: You don't own this place!
SIMON: Neither do you!
FRANK: *What* did you say?
RACHEL: He said you don't own it either.
KIDS: No!
MAGGIE: Cheeky monkeys!
KIDS: Cheeky monkeys!

> *The* KIDS *imitate monkeys.*

FRANK: Stop mocking your elders! We want peace and quiet!

JOHN: Being quiet's boring.
KIDS: Boring!
OLDIES: Quiet!
KIDS (*chanting*): Boring!

> Enter JACKIE. *She rings the bell. Silence.*

JACKIE: Where are your teachers?
KIDS: Pub.
JACKIE: I beg your pardon?
ANN (*mock-genteel*): They have gone to the public house.

> The KIDS *giggle.*

JACKIE: Typical! Just play quietly.

> *Exit* JACKIE.

WINNIE: It isn't right, leaving them to go off boozing.
CHARLIE: Teachers! Huh! I wouldn't pay 'em in washers!
PENNY: Our teacher has booked all the hostels for the wrong
    month as well, hasn't he?
KIDS: Yeah!
ANDREW: And we've just started a sponsored walk for £10,000,
    and we can't finish it, can we?
KIDS: No!
WINNIE: Well, I never! No wonder you're fed up.
JOHN: Would you like a crisp?
POLLY: Ee, just one. Thank you very much!

> JOHN *offers crisps to the other* OLDIES, *who thank him and take
> one.*

PERCY: I'm surprised you've room to eat after your meal.
RACHEL: Meal? Do you know what they gave us? Soup!
KIDS: Celery soup! Yucch!
POLLY: Soup won't fill you. What did you have for lunch?
RACHEL: Ratty sandwiches. I didn't eat mine.

> *She holds up a plastic bag containing a mashed-up pinkish mass.
> Laughter.*

RACHEL: Jam sandwich!

MAGGIE: Did you others eat all your lunch?

KIDS: No!

MAGGIE: What a waste! What have you got left?

One after another the KIDS *produce plastic bags and chant their contents.*

ANDREW: Bread.

ANN: Raisins.

CARLTON: Jam sandwich.

BETH: Chocolate.

JOHN: Apple.

CLARE: Raisins.

PAUL: Bread.

EMMA: More bread.

SIMON: Even more bread.

PENNY: Raisins.

TIM: More raisins.

RACHEL: And another apple.

WILLIAM: And another jam sandwich.

SARAH: And bread, more bread.

MAGGIE: That sounds just about right.

She whispers to the other WOMEN, *who smile and nod.*

RACHEL: Just right for what?

Enter JACKIE.

JACKIE: Everybody happy?

ALL: Yes!

JACKIE: No more falling out?

ALL: No!

JACKIE: That's nice.

POLLY: Could you let us have some eggs and milk?

JACKIE: I think so. What's it for?

POLLY: It's a secret. And have you a big pan?

JACKIE: Come through and I'll show you.

The WOMEN *go through the inner door.* JACKIE *follows them and the lights go out.* ALL *scream or exclaim.* JACKIE *re-enters with lantern.*

HERBERT: Whatever's the matter?

JACKIE: The generator's stopped. Probably run out of fuel. Use this. There's another in the kitchen.

JACKIE *puts the lantern on the table and exits.*

ANDREW: I can't see to read.

SARAH: It's spooky.

RACHEL: Yes. We ought to play a spooky game.

BETH: No!

KIDS: Yes!

SARAH *(to the* MEN*)*: Do you know any spooky games?

CHARLIE: Spooky? Have you ever seen a ouija board?

KIDS: No.

CHARLIE: The women used to scare each other to death with one.

MEN: They did that!

CHARLIE *(standing)*: Did I see some letters?

ANN: It's Scrabble.

CHARLIE: Just the job. Spread the letters round the edge of the table. You girls, come and sit round. We haven't got a planchette: go and get a glass.

Exit CLARE.

BETH: Does it hurt?

CHARLIE: No, it's just a bit of fun.

Re-enter CLARE *with a glass.*

CHARLIE: Put it in the middle of the table. Upside-down. That's it. *(The* GIRLS *gather round.)*

CHARLIE: You boys watch. Shhh! All touch the glass. *(The* GIRLS *do.)* Now ask it a question.

CARLTON: What is 79 times 82?

PAUL: What will be Number One in the charts next week?

GIRLS: Shut up!

CHARLIE: Shhh! You boys, simmer down! Now, girls, touch the glass very gently: don't push it. That's grand. Now is there anything you want to know that a friend in the spirit world can tell us?

BETH: Ooh!

GIRLS: Shhh!

ANN *(raising a hand)*: Can I ask a question?

CHARLIE: Ask it quietly.

ANN: This is my question: How can we get £10,000 for our minibus if we can't do our sponsored walk?

> KIDS *mutter agreement.*

CHARLIE: Hush! Let it answer. How can these children get £10,000 for their minibus? All concentrate. Boys, close your eyes. Let the glass have its way. What will it spell?

> *The glass moves.*

CHARLIE: It's moving!

ALL: Ahh!

> *The* BOYS *open their eyes.*

CHARLIE: What does it say?

> *As the glass moves, the* KIDS *chant the letters.*

KIDS: T – A – P. Tap. I – N. In. Tap in.

> *The glass stops.*

SARAH: What's that mean: 'Tap in'?

CHARLIE: Shh! Let it finish!

BETH: Ooh, it's moving again!

KIDS: Shh! T – A – P. Tap. Tap in tap.

CARLTON: *(very clearly)*: Tap in tap.

PAUL: That's rubbish: Tap in tap.

The BOYS *agree. The lights come on.*

ALL: Aw!

JACKIE *enters.*

JACKIE: Back to normal! Who's been playing with the fuel tap?
   And what's this glass doing here?

She takes the glass and the lantern.

EMMA: Oh, can't we go on playing?
GIRLS: Yes!
BOYS: No!
CHARLIE: No, it's had its say.
EMMA: How did it move?
TIM: Because you all pushed it.
GIRLS: No! I didn't. It moved itself.
JACKIE: Hey! Who promised to be quiet?

   Enter JESSIE, *followed by* WINNIE *and* POLLY *carrying dishes
   and spoons.*

JESSIE: Dishes out! Spoons out! Be quick!
PAUL: What's this for?
JESSIE: You'll see. All got a dish? Right, Maggie!
WOMEN: A little of what you fancy does you good!

   Enter MAGGIE *carrying a large pan. The* WOMEN *cheer.*

MAGGIE (*holding up the ladle*): This'll fill your bellies! Who's first?
   Don't kill each other in the rush!

   The KIDS *peer into the pan.*

KIDS: Ugh!
JOHN: What's that mess supposed to be?
WOMEN: Bread and butter pudding!
KIDS: What?
MAGGIE: Bread and butter pudding: to fill you up!
JESSIE: It's delicious!

SIMON: It looks like sick.

Laughter.

WINNIE: It's got plump raisins.
POLLY: And eggs.
MAGGIE: And it's very good for you.
SIMON: It still looks like sick.

Laughter.

FRANK: I'll have some.
MAGGIE: You won't! You've just had a good meal. Who's going to try it?

The KIDS *sit scowling.*

MAGGIE: Who's brave enough to give it a taste?

PAUL, *grinning, raises his hand.*

PAUL: Just a bit.

MAGGIE *ladles a small amount onto his dish while all the* KIDS *stare.*

WILLIAM: Where do you want to be buried, kid?

Laughter.

MAGGIE: Shhh! He's tasting it!

Slowly, PAUL *takes a tiny amount and savours it, then he takes a spoonful and swallows it. His eyes light up.*

PAUL: Magic! Can I have some more?
JOHN: Can I have some?

The KIDS *crowd round demanding a helping.*

MAGGIE: Sit down! There's enough for everybody!

They sit holding out their dishes. She ladles it out.

MAGGIE: All say after me:
Bread and butter pud,

Golden brown.
Open your gob
And gollup it down.

The KIDS *repeat each line after her.*

MAGGIE: Very good! All got some? Right, start!

The KIDS *start to eat. Enter* JACKIE *with a newspaper.*

JACKIE: Everybody happy?
ALL: Mmm!
JACKIE: Good. Anyone lost this?
PERCY: That's mine! Where did you find it?
JACKIE: Behind the cooker.
SIMON: I loved that. What's for breakfast?
JACKIE: What about scrambled egg?

SIMON *pulls a face and says 'Aw!'*

JACKIE: Don't say it!
SIMON: It looks like sick.

Laughter.

WINNIE: You're like the lad who saw a Scotsman with a bowl of
porridge and said to him, 'Are you going to have that for your
breakfast, or have you just had it?'

The KIDS *groan.*

WINNIE: Well, I bet you don't know any better jokes.

During the following, the WOMEN *collect and take out the
dishes.*

WILLIAM: Wanna bet? Knock, knock!
POLLY: Who's there?
WILLIAM: Aardvark.
POLLY: Aardvark who?
WILLIAM *(singing)*: Aardvark a million miles for one of your
smiles!

Laughter.

SARAH: Knock, knock!
OLDIES: Who's there?
SARAH: Wendy.
OLDIES: Wendy who?
SARAH *(singing)*: Wendy red, red, robin comes bob, bob,
   bobbing along, along!

   Laughter. Enter WOMEN *with blankets.*

PERCY: What do you call two burglars? A pair of nickers!

   The KIDS *groan.*

WINNIE: Percy! Don't be rude!
ANN: What tree can't you climb?
KIDS *(pulling a chain)*: A lavatree!

   OLDIES *groan.*

BETH: Knock, knock!
OLDIES: Who's there?
BETH: Sal.
OLDIES: Sal who?
KIDS *(singing)*: Salong way to Tipperary,
ALL: It's a long way to go.
   It's a long way to Tipperary

   Enter JACKIE *with blankets.*

ALL: To the sweetest girl I know . . .

   ALL *look at* JACKIE *and stop singing.*

JACKIE *(to the* OLDIES*)*: I seem to remember somebody asking
   for peace and quiet!
KIDS *(pointing)*: They did!
JACKIE: Well, it's time we had some. It's nearly time for lights
   out.
KIDS: Oh, no!

JACKIE: Oh, yes! These are all the spare blankets, so you'll have to sleep in your clothes. Here!

She and the WOMEN *throw out the blankets.*

JACKIE: Boys this side; girls there.
POLLY: Come on, you men: bedtime!
MEN: Aw, no!
POLLY: Don't you start! These kiddies need an early start.

Grumbling, the MEN *rise.*

MAGGIE: Good night, children!
KIDS: 'Night!
JESSIE: Sweet dreams!
KIDS: Sweet dreams!
CARLTON: Thanks for the pudding.
WINNIE: And thanks for the jokes. *(To* JACKIE*)* Good night.
JACKIE: Good night.

The OLDIES *go out and the* KIDS *find places to sleep.*

RACHEL: What if Sir and Miss come back late?
JACKIE: We'll lock 'em out, eh?
KIDS: Yeah!
JACKIE: Settle down now.

They settle down, BOYS *on one side,* GIRLS *on the other.*

JACKIE: I can hear them coming now.
RACHEL: Lock the door!
KIDS: Yeah! Please!
JACKIE: Shush! All lie down and pretend to sleep: quick! Keep still! 'Night!

Exit JACKIE.

SIMON: Why do we have to . . .
KIDS: Shhh!

They all lie still.

SIR *(singing off)*: Ha ha ha, he he he,
>   Little brown jug don't I love thee?

The door opens and the TEACHERS enter, MISS first.

SIR: Ha ha ha, he he he . . .
MISS: Sh!
SIR: They're all dead!
MISS: Don't be silly, Raymond: they're asleep. Don't disturb them.
SIR: Poor little souls! Where shall we go tomorrow?
MISS: Go to sleep. Here's a blanket. Good night, Raymond.
SIR: Good night, Gwyneth!

They look at each other, then meet Down Centre.

SIR: Oh, Gwyneth!
MISS: Oh, Raymond!

They kiss. The KIDS look up.

BOYS: Oh, Gwyneth!
GIRLS: Oh, Raymond!

The TEACHERS leap apart.

MISS: Lie down and don't be stupid!

Laughing, the KIDS lie down instantly. MISS lies down.

SIR: Be quiet.

He puts the lights out. There is still some light. He lies down.

SIR: Now, good night.
KIDS: 'Night, sir.

Silence. One or two yawn or move slightly, but soon all are silent. A clock begins to strike eleven. The inner door opens and JACKIE enters with a torch. She crosses to the outer door and locks it, then crosses, shines her torch round the room and exits. The clock finishes striking. Silence. From somewhere come three or four bursts of tapping, then silence again.

The lights come up. The TEACHERS *rouse and sit.*

MISS: Good morning.

SIR: Good morning. Someone was clattering about during the night. Not one of ours.

SIMON: Sir! Sir! It was one of them hike-hitchers! I saw 'em when I went to the bog.

>   *Some* KIDS *laugh.*

MISS: Went to the *what*?

SIMON *(pointing outside)*: Miss, the bog.

MISS *(pointing inside)*: You mean the toilet!

SIMON *(looking inside)*: Aw, I didn't know there was a toilet.

>   *Some* KIDS *laugh.* OTHERS *begin to wake.*

MISS *(folding her blanket)*: Of course there are toilets! I'll go and see if the kitchen's free.

>   *Exit* MISS.

SIR: Wake up, children!

ANDREW: Aw, we're in this place.

MISS *(entering)*: No one in the kitchen. The warden says to make scrambled eggs.

ANDREW: Sir, what are we going to do today?

SIR: Walk to the town and catch a bus home.

SARAH: But what about the minibus fund?

MISS: We'll have to try again next year, won't we?

KIDS: Aw, miss!

SIR: Stop moaning and fold your blankets. Then go and wash while we make breakfast. Move!

>   *The* KIDS *go out grumbling. The* TEACHERS *pile the blankets.*

SIR: Raining again.

MISS: The whole trip's a wash-out.

SIR: Let's put the eggs on.

>   *As they cross to the door,* LIZ *and* TRISH *enter with their luggage.*

SIR: Good morning!

> LIZ *and* TRISH *ignore him and put down their luggage. The* TEACHERS *go out.* LIZ *and* TRISH *look rapidly round, apparently searching.*

LIZ: It must be here.

TRISH: Why must it?

LIZ: 'Cause we've looked everywhere else, birdbrain! Get looking again.

> *They tap the floor and walls. Enter* JACKIE.

JACKIE: There you are. Not going, are you?

LIZ: No, we lost something.

JACKIE: Well, when you've found it, come and pay your debts. And what duty will you do?

LIZ: We'll sweep in here.

JACKIE: Right.

> *Exit* JACKIE. *They search by the fire. Enter* HERBERT *and* PERCY.

HERBERT: Lost something?

LIZ: No.

PERCY: Well, I'm going to read this paper now, even if it is a day late.

> *They sit and read.* LIZ *searches behind* HERBERT.

HERBERT: What are you up to?

LIZ: *(sighing and looking round)*: We're not up to anything. Do you know what this place was called when it was a pub?

HERBERT: Er, Red something, wasn't it, Percy?

PERCY: Lion. Red Lion.

LIZ *(to* TRISH*)*: You wally! Red Lion! We've been wasting our time! Come on!

> LIZ *and* TRISH *pick up their luggage and leave. Enter* JACKIE *with brush and dustpan.*

PERCY: By gum, this is interesting!

JACKIE: Have you seen those two girls?

HERBERT: They just went out.

JACKIE: That is the end! I get up at half-past six to make them an early breakfast, then they slope off without paying! It makes you sick!

Enter the KIDS.

JACKIE: And somebody has pulled a tap off in the women's washroom!

CLARE: It wasn't one of us, was it?

GIRLS: No.

JACKIE: Well, all the duties are to do. One on each card. Who's going to sweep this room?

CARLTON *raises a hand. She gives him a card and a brush.*

JACKIE: Here!

Enter TEACHERS.

JACKIE: Take these cards! Get 'em working!

SIR: Actually, our eggs are ...

JACKIE: Don't push me too far! Brushes in the kitchen!

She storms out.

ANDREW: Don't argue with her, sir: she's worse than you.

MISS *(looking at the cards)*: Right, these are our duties.

PENNY: Aw, do we have to do 'em?

TEACHERS: Yes!

PENNY: Aw!

KIDS: Shut up!

MISS: Do these duties fast, then breakfast will be ready. Mop men's washrooms and clean basins.

ANDREW and JOHN: Us! *(They grab the card and go out.)*

MISS: Mop women's washroom.

ANN and BETH: We'll do that. *(They take the card and go out.)*

MISS: Here, sort the rest out yourselves. (*The* KIDS *take the cards and look through them.*)

CLARE: Come on, Emma, we'll clean the kitchen. (*They go out.*)

PAUL: Help me with the dustbins, kid.

SIMON: OK. (*They go out.*)

PENNY (*to* RACHEL *and* SARAH): Come and sweep the hall.

RACHEL *and* SARAH: Right. (*They go out*).

TIM: We can clean up outside, William.

WILLIAM: Aw, not in this weather!

TIM: Come on, it's got to be done.

> *They go out and only* CARLTON *is left sweeping. The* TEACHERS *put the kit on the table to help him.*

PERCY (*reading*): Just how stupid can they get?

SIR: Oh dear, what have they done now?

PERCY: Not your children. In the paper here: £25,000.

MISS: Stolen, is it?

PERCY: No, some sort of daft prize. Here.

HERBERT (*taking the paper and reading*): 'Treasure Trove. This week's prize money has risen to a staggering £25,000, hidden somewhere in England. Solve the rhyming clue and the money could be yours.'

> *The* OTHERS *turn, but he reads silently.*

FRANK: Well?

HERBERT: Well what?

OTHERS: What's the clue?

HERBERT: Some silly poetry. Here.

> *He gives the paper to* MISS, *who reads aloud.*

MISS: 'On moorland high
    Where drink is dry
    And once hung emerald male,
    See angles three:
    A tap's the key.
    Find gold instead of ale.'

FRANK: Isn't it barmy?

Enter the WOMEN *dressed for outdoors and carrying their cycle-bags.*

MAGGIE: Are you men going to stay here all day?

The WOMEN *go out of the outer door. There is a knock at the inner door and* SARAH *peeps in.*

SARAH: Miss, we've finished all our duties. Is breakfast ready?
MISS: Not yet. The gas is very low. Come in here.

The KIDS *enter grumbling and sit gloomily round the tables.*

EMMA: It's pouring down.
BETH: We'll get soaked!
PENNY: They'll all laugh at us at school when we haven't done the walk.
KIDS: Yeah.
CLARE: We kept saying how much money we were going to raise.
RACHEL: And we all had our pictures taken for the paper. Is that what you're reading, miss?
MISS: No. There's a competition in here.
TIM: I never win competitions.
WILLIAM: My auntie won a bottle of whisky.
SIMON: I won a goldfish at the fair, but it died.

Laughter.

RACHEL: What's the prize in the paper?
MISS: Only £25,000.
KIDS: Twenty-five thousand!
ANDREW: What do you have to do?
MISS: Solve a clue.
HERBERT: It's all in rhyme.
ANDREW: We've got the time.

Laughter. Enter the WOMEN *in a rage.*

JESSIE: That is the end!

MAGGIE: All our tyres let down! Who's done it? Own up!

PAUL: It wasn't one of us.

ANN: We haven't been outside, have we?

KIDS: No, we haven't.

POLLY: Well, who else is there?

CHARLIE: What about those hitch-hikers?

WINNIE: You're right! And they've taken all our pumps!

The MEN *laugh.*

WINNIE: And yours!

MEN: What!

The KIDS *laugh.*

HERBERT *(to* PERCY*)*: And they hid your paper so you couldn't read the clue!

SIR: So that's why they were sneaking about in the night!

MISS: Do you think they found the money here?

HERBERT: Not they. One of 'em said they'd been wasting their time, just before they left.

MAGGIE: Have they gone? What about our pumps?

FRANK: Forget that. Why were they looking here? How does this place fit the clue?

SIR: Let's read it again. 'On moorland high': that fits here, right?

ALL: Right.

SIR: 'Where drink is dry'. What can that mean?

HERBERT: It means that this place used to be a pub and have a licence, but now it's dry.

JACKIE *(entering)*: You can't stay here long. I want to clear the place before I lock up.

POLLY: There must be hundreds of old pubs. Why should it mean this one?

HERBERT: Let's see. What's the next bit?

SIR: 'And once hung emerald male.'

FRANK: Rubbish!

SIR: 'See angles three.'

FRANK: More rubbish! We're nowhere near the sea.
SIR: No: S–E–E. You see three angles.
PERCY: Still rubbish. Forget it.

    He takes the paper.

CARLTON: It isn't rubbish! Why did those hitch–hikers come all
    that way? They were following the clue! What's the rest of it?
PERCY: Here. You read it.
CARLTON: 'A tap's the key.' They pulled the taps off in the
    washroom! Why? Because they were looking for the gold!
MISS: Perhaps they were wrong.
CARLTON: 'Where once hung emerald male.' What can it mean?

    ALL *shrug.*

WILLIAM: Must have been the inn sign when it was a pub. It
    must have been called The Emerald Male.

    Laughter.

TIM *(leaping up)*: I've got it!
PAUL: Well, keep it to yourself.
TIM: No! Watch!
MISS: Oh, not 'Give Us A Clue'?

    TIM *nods and mimes pulling a pint.*

ALL: Beer! A pub!

    He holds up three fingers.

ALL: Three words!

    He holds up one finger.

ALL: First word!

    He makes a 'T'.

ALL: The! The . . .

    He holds up two fingers.

ALL: Second word!

He thinks, then holds up three fingers.

ALL: Third word!

He points to FRANK.

ALL: Cyclist. Hosteller. Grandad. Old man. Man. Man! The something man.

He touches his ear.

ALL: Sounds like.

He walks round, waving an arm stiffly.

ANDREW: Puppet!
ANN: Zombie!
CARLTON: General!
BETH: Queen!

TIM *nods.*

BETH: Queen! Sounds like queen.
SIMON: King?

Laughter.

PAUL: Mean!
CLARE: Keen!
WILLIAM: Bean!
EMMA: Green!

TIM *nods.*

EMMA: Green? Green what?
WILLIAM: Green! It's the Green Man!

Re-enter JACKIE, carrying luggage.

JACKIE: This place is closing. You'll all have to go now.
SIR: Wait, please! What was this place called when it was a pub?
JACKIE: Something coloured.

SIR: What colour?

Pause: JACKIE *thinks.*

JACKIE: Red! The Red Lion!
ALL: Aw!
JACKIE: Come on: move!
WILLIAM: Please! What was it called before that?
JACKIE: You're the second person to ask me that, but I can't remember. Let's go.
WILLIAM: It was the Green Man, wasn't it?
JACKIE *(stopping)*: That's right: The Green Man.
EMMA: Angles three! A triangle! It's the sign for a youth hostel on maps and things! Look!

She points to a map/notice.

ALL: Yes!

ALL *applaud.*

JACKIE *(putting down her luggage)*: Are you all off your rockers? What does it matter?

ALL *begin talking at once. She rings the bell.*

JACKIE: I'll give you one minute to explain what you're all raving about, then I'm locking up.
MISS: There's a competition in this paper to win £25,000. We think the money is hidden somewhere in this hostel. The final clue is 'A tap's the key.'
JACKIE: How could it be hidden here? Move!
PAUL: No! We're not moving! We're going to find the money! Aren't we, kids?
KIDS: Yes!
SIR: Where are all the taps?
JACKIE *(sitting with a sigh)*: Washrooms, kitchen.

Most KIDS *exclaim and run out of the inner door.*

JACKIE: Oh, and there's a very old tap in the outside wash-house.

JOHN, PAUL *and* CARLTON *run out of the outside door.*
Most KIDS *drift back through the inner door.*

PENNY: Nothing, miss.
ANDREW: Here's John.

JOHN *runs in, followed by* PAUL *and* CARLTON.

MISS: Well?
JOHN: Nothing at all.
KIDS: Aw!
SIR: Any more taps?
JACKIE: No. Get moving!
FRANK: I know: the cellar!
ALL: Yes!

Some KIDS *are on their toes, ready to run.*

FRANK: Where's the cellar door?
JACKIE: There isn't one.
FRANK: No cellar door?
JACKIE: No cellar. We're built on solid rock. No cellar, no more
taps, no more wasting my time.
SIR: Well, we tried. Shoulder your packs!

Grumbling, the SCHOOL PARTY *prepare to leave.*

JACKIE *(to the* OLDIES*)*: The bloke down at the pub'll lend you
a cycle-pump. I'll have to lock up now.

The OLDIES *stand. The* KIDS *are beginning to drift out.*

JACKIE: Oh, I must turn the water off.

Exit JACKIE.

HERBERT: If there was no cellar, where did they keep the beer?
PERCY: In here. This room would have been the bar-room, or
the tap-room, more likely ...
MISS: The *what?*
PERCY *(startled)*: I'm saying: this would be called the tap-room.
Or just – the tap.

MISS: The *tap*! *This* is the tap? Think! Tap!

SARAH: She must have had a tap on the head!

EMMA: No! Remember! The ouija board said 'Tap in tap'. And this is the tap!

SARAH: But there isn't a tap in here, is there?

EMMA: Not a water tap! Like you said: tap on the head.

MISS: Right! Tap on the floor! Tap on the walls! Tap on the ceiling! Tap everywhere! Everybody!

She starts tapping on the floor.

MISS: Spread out! Tap! The money must be here!

PAUL *(by the door)*: You've got to come back! Miss is going round the bend!

The KIDS *who have gone out return.*

SIMON: What's wrong with her?

MISS: Tap! Everybody! *(To the* OLDIES*)* And you!

Startled, ALL *start tapping, lightly and rapidly. Soon,* ALL *are tapping to the same rhythm. Enter* JACKIE.

JACKIE: What on earth is happening?

ALL *(fingers to lips)*: Shhh!

JACKIE: I shall go mad!

CARLTON, *by the bar where* PORTER *was first seen, gives three loud bangs on the bar.* ALL *stop and look.*

CARLTON: Sir! Listen!

He bangs again.

SIR: It's hollow! It's opening! It's empty!

ALL: Aw!

CARLTON: No money: just a bit of paper.

SIR: What paper?

CARLTON *(producing it)*: This.

SIR *(reading it: triumphant)*: Ta–dah!

MISS: What's it say?

Tap Tap

SIR *(reading)*: '*Daily News* Treasure Trove Contest. Congratulations! You are the winner ...

ALL *start talking.*

GIRLS: Shhh!

SIR *(reading)*: 'You are the winner if you claim your £25,000 before 10 a.m. on October 14th.'

CARLTON: That's today!

MISS: What time is it?

JACKIE: Just about ten. How do you claim?

SIR: Ring this number: Moorfield 99.

JACKIE: That's the number of the call-box at the end of the lane.

SIR: A call-box?

A clock starts to strike.

MISS: Ring!

SIR: What?

MISS *(running to the phone)*: Ninety nine! *(She dials.)* I wish to claim the £25,000. At the hostel.

The clock starts to chime ten.

MISS: He's coming. With the money.

Cheers.

JACKIE *(looking out)*: There's a Land Rover coming up the lane.

ALL *talk. There is a loud knock on the door.*

JACKIE: Come in!

Enter PORTER *carrying five canvas cash-bags.*

PORTER: Hello again!

JACKIE: You hid that note yesterday! You're not a worker.

PORTER: I work for the *Daily News*, sunshine. And I have here £25,000 in gold sovereigns. Who is claiming the prize?

Silence. ALL *look at each other.*

PENNY: We found it, so it's ours.

JACKIE: No. You found it in my hostel, so it belongs here.

PAUL: That's not fair!

ALL *begin to chatter loudly.* WINNIE *rings the bell.*

WINNIE: Less arguing! *(To the* TEACHERS*)* How much does your school need for its minibus fund?

TEACHERS }
KIDS } : Ten thousand pounds.

WINNIE *(giving two bags)*: Five thousand. Ten thousand.

The KIDS *applaud.*

WINNIE: And how much do you need to finish rebuilding your hostel?

JACKIE: Ten thousand pounds.

WINNIE: *(handing over two bags)*: Five thousand, ten thousand. You needn't close now. Five thousand left over.

Enter LIZ *and* TRISH.

LIZ: We've just had an idea about . . .

KIDS: We've found it!

TRISH }
LIZ } : Aw!

JACKIE *gives* LIZ *Carlton's brush and dustpan.*

JACKIE: Never mind. You'll find that the kitchen needs sweeping.

LIZ: Aw, no.

Exit LIZ *to the kitchen.*

JACKIE: And you can put those bike-pumps back. And blow the tyres up.

Exit TRISH.

WINNIE: What about the extra five thousand?

PERCY: Well, we do need a new meeting-hut, and it was my newspaper that you used.

ANN *(crossing to* PERCY *with the last bag)*: Five thousand pounds
  to the Autumn Leaves for a new hut!

  Applause.

MAGGIE: Now is everybody happy?
ALL: Yes!
RACHEL: No!
MAGGIE: No? Why not?
RACHEL: Because I'm starving, that's why.
PENNY: So am I!

  Murmurs of agreement.

SIR: No problem: the eggs are ready!

  Enter LIZ *with a smoking pan.*

LIZ: These belong to anybody?
MISS *(snatching the pan)*: Raymond! You've burnt our breakfast!

  She hurls the pan into the kitchen. LIZ *exclaims and rushes off.*

KIDS: Aw!
JOHN: He's useless! Get him!

  The KIDS *advance on* SIR.

JESSIE: Hold your horses! Don't spoil the fun! There's another big
  pan in the kitchen still half-full of lovely grub! Know what I
  mean?
ALL: Bread and butter pud!
JESSIE: Correct! The finest food in the world!
SIMON: Can you eat it for breakfast?
JESSIE: You can eat it anytime! I'll go and warm it up and we'll
  all have a big helping to celebrate winning the money!

  Cheers.

MISS: It's raining worse than ever. What say I ring for a coach to
  take us home?
KIDS: Yes!

MISS *goes to the phone, dials and talks quietly during the following.*

RACHEL: We never had a sing-song last night.

FRANK: Let's have one now while we wait for the pud.

MISS: The coach will be here in half an hour.

FRANK: All on your feet! First song! The chorus is 'Bread and Butter Pud'. Ready?

ALL: Yes!

FRANK: Off we go!

> One Christmas Eve in the middle of the war
> The Jerries were giving us hell,
> When into the mud beside us flew
> A most unusual shell.
> My closest friend unscrewed the end
> As in the trench it stood,
> And found that shell completely full of

ALL: Bread and Butter Pud!

MAGGIE: I used to know a farmer
> And he had a herd of cows.
> But they refused to graze on grass
> When he turned 'em out to browse.
> So he called the vet who said 'Look, my pet,
> That green stuff is no good:
> Cows don't want grass: they need a mass of

ALL: Bread and Butter Pud!'

HERBERT There was a Yorkshire cyclist
> Who got punctures in his tyres
> From nails and glass and hawthorn twigs
> And razor-blades and wires.
> He tried to mend the holes with glue
> But it wasn't any good.
> Now he sticks his patches on with lots of

ALL: Bread and Butter Pud!

WINNIE: There was a famous surgeon
Who got more and more distressed
'Cause he couldn't cure a patient
Of a rash upon his chest.
Then he found the answer in a book
From the time of Robin Hood:
And slapped on a steaming poultice made of

ALL: Bread and Butter Pud!

Enter JESSIE *with a large pan.*

JESSIE: Now, Highlanders love haggis
And they always ask for more,
And Welshmen live on seaweed
That they gather on the shore.
Frenchmen swear by truffles
That they dig up in the wood,
But there's nothing in the world to equal

ALL: Bread and Butter Pud!

[*Curtain.*]